The Life of Jesus
of Nazareth

TOLD BY ERMA FERRARI

PICTURES BY WILLIAM HOLE, R.S.A., R.E.

SIMON AND SCHUSTER ★ NEW YORK

TABLE OF CONTENTS

The Angel Gabriel hails the Virgin Mary and announces to her that she will be the mother of a son.

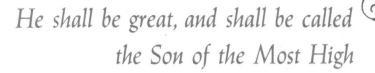

He shall be great, and shall be called the Son of the Most High

A STILLNESS LAY over the town of Nazareth. The hot afternoon sun beat down upon the market place and filtered through the narrow streets. Mary, the young daughter of Anne and Joachim, had been to the well to fetch water for the evening meal. The coolness of the house was pleasant after the long walk, but it seemed very quiet. Was it her marriage to Joseph, soon to take place, that made her feel as if something was about to happen?

"Mary." An unfamiliar voice spoke her name, although no one had entered the house. The voice came again: "Mary, thou who art highly favored." The girl looked up. An angel stood before her. "The Lord is with thee," he said. "Blessed art thou among women."

Had she fallen asleep? No, there was the water jug just where she had put it down. There was Mother's cloak on its peg. But what strange words, were these?

"Thou shalt bring forth a son, and thou shalt call his name Jesus. He shall be great, and shall be called the Son of the Most High."

How could the angel's words be true, since Joseph was not yet her husband? "How shall this be?" she asked.

"The Holy Ghost shall come upon thee; that which is to be born shall be called holy, the Son of God."

The shock, the mystery of it filled Mary with wonder. But the angel reassured her. Elisabeth, her aged cousin, was also to bear a son. She, too, had experienced a miracle at God's hands.

Humbly, Mary said to the angel, "Behold the handmaid of the Lord: Be it unto me according to thy word."

My soul doth magnify the Lord

IT WAS a long journey from Nazareth to the city in Judea where Elisabeth and her husband Zacharias lived. It would take four days of uncomfortable joggling on a little donkey to cover the one hundred miles. But as Mary and a companion rode and walked slowly down through the hills of Galilee, Mary relived the history of her people.

Not far south of Nazareth they passed Shunem, where the prophet Elisha had performed his miracles. A few hours later, they stopped near Mount Gilboa where Saul and Jonathan had died.

On the fourth day of their journey, the gleaming white towers of the temple at Jerusalem appeared through a gorge in the bare Judean hills. But they went on until they came to Hebron. They rode through the gates of the ancient town, past the noisy beggars, the eager merchants, the laborers waiting to be hired.

Before the door of Zacharias' comfortable home, Mary and Elisabeth greeted one another. The older woman felt her unborn child stir within her. What did this mean? She looked at Mary thoughtfully.

"Cousin Elisabeth," Mary said, "I have much to tell you."

But there was no need for Mary to share her secret. Suddenly Elisabeth knew.

"Blessed art thou among women," Elisabeth said. "And whence is this to me, that the mother of my Lord should come to me?" Tenderly, Elisabeth clasped her cousin's hands.

At this generous, reverent greeting from her beloved kinswoman, Mary's heart overflowed with gratitude and joy, and she raised her voice in praise to God. "My soul doth magnify the Lord."

Mary goes into the hill country of Judea and salutes Elisabeth.

Joseph and Mary arrive at Bethlehem, but there is no room for them in the inn.

And she brought forth her first-born son

THE FESTIVE wedding days were long since over, and Mary and Joseph had set up their new home in Joseph's carpentry shop. As she did her work, Mary listened to the sound of Joseph's tools that were busily shaping plows and yokes.

There was extra baking to be done today, for soon they would be setting out on the trip to Bethlehem. Bethlehem was Joseph's birthplace, and he must return there to register for the census of the Roman Empire. Perhaps, Mary thought, she should remain at home, for the baby was soon to be born. But she wanted Joseph to be with her at the infant's birth.

The ninety-mile trip south to Bethlehem was tiring and uncomfortable, but there were things to enjoy along the way. Sometimes Mary and Joseph stopped to rest near clumps of purple anemones and gay cyclamen that brightened a hillside. All the roads were crowded with people returning to the places of their birth, and there was pleasant talk among old friends and new acquaintances. On the fifth day of the journey, Mary caught her first glimpse of the little white town of Bethlehem, perched on two hills. It brought a thrill to her heart, for this would be the birthplace of her son.

Within the town itself, Mary and Joseph found noise and confusion everywhere. The one inn was filled. But, the innkeeper explained, the young wife could be made comfortable in the animals' quarters nearby.

And so, beside quietly feeding cattle, Mary's son was born. Tenderly, she laid the sleeping child in the big stone manger, made soft and warm with fragrant hay from the Judean hills of the land of David.

THE MIDNIGHT WATCH was nearly over before Bethlehem grew quiet. But at last all the visitors had found lodgings or had pitched their tents outside the city walls.

Not all the people of Bethlehem were asleep. Up in the hills, a group of shepherds were guarding their flocks from the dangers of the night. Now and then they sang softly to the sound of a flute. *When I consider thy heavens, the moon and the stars which thou hast ordained, what is man that thou art mindful of him?*

"The stars are very bright tonight," young Nathan, the flute player, said. "And how close they seem."

His father nodded sleepily. "Father! Father! Look!"

A dazzling light had enveloped the hillside. Terrified, the shepherds fell to their knees as an angel appeared within the light.

"Fear not," the angel said. "For behold I bring you good tidings of great joy, which shall be to all people. For unto you is born this day, in the city of David, a Saviour which is Christ the Lord."

What words were these? Could it be true that the long-awaited Messiah had come? Wonderingly, the shepherds listened as the angel spoke again. "Ye shall find the babe, wrapped in swaddling clothes, lying in a manger."

And suddenly the hillside rang with the song of a host of angels, praising God and saying, "Glory to God in the highest, and on earth peace, good will toward men."

And so to humble shepherds had come the first news of the birth of him who one day would be called the Good Shepherd.

14

An angel announces to the shepherds of Bethlehem the birth of Jesus.

15

The shepherds proceed to Bethlehem and find the infant lying in a manger.

16

Let us now go
even unto Bethlehem and see

I T WAS quiet again on the hillside. The angels had disappeared, and only the stars shone out in the sky.

"Had we not all witnessed the messengers from heaven, I would say I had been dreaming," one of the shepherds said. The others nodded, still too moved to speak.

"Father!" Nathan could wait no longer for the older men to gather their wits. "Let us now go even unto Bethlehem. The angels said we would find the babe there, lying in a manger."

"There are many mangers in Bethlehem," his father said. "As many mangers as there are caves for the cattle. And the city is crowded with visitors tonight."

"But we can find him if we search. The angel said so. Come, let us make haste!"

So, leaving the precious flocks, the shepherds went down the hillside, rods and staffs in hand. Past the visitors' tents outside the wall and through the gates into the dark, silent town they went, looking for a newborn child. And finally, in a stable-cave cut neatly out of a rocky slope, they knew their search was ended. No ordinary mother was this bending over the stone manger. Quietly, hesitatingly, the shepherds approached. Could this sleeping infant be the Messiah, the chosen deliverer of Israel? With awe, they bent over the manger. Joseph sat at one side, patiently quiet.

"The babe's name is Jesus," the young mother said.

Even unlearned shepherds knew the meaning of that name—*God saves*. Reverently, they knelt before their King.

*For mine eyes
have seen thy salvation*

CROWDS thronged through the gates of the wall that surrounded the temple in Jerusalem. In the Court of the Gentiles, the loud talk of money-changers mingled with the bleating of lambs.

Mary, with her infant son in her arms, looked around as she waited for Joseph. He had gone to one of the many booths to buy the least costly offering that would be acceptable for sacrifice on the temple altars. Today they were presenting their son to God, as the Law of Moses demanded.

With a pair of doves, newly killed and blessed, Joseph joined Mary and they crossed the Court of the Gentiles. Proud of their race and heritage, they walked past the signs that warned all Gentiles to go no further. They made their way to the Inner Court, then up to the Court of the Priests. Reverently, Mary carried her little son up the fifteen steps to the sacrificial altars. Here she offered her sacrifice at the altar fires and held up her son for the priest's blessing.

A strange man waited with Joseph at the foot of the steps. He was an elderly person, and he watched Mary closely as she came down the steps with her child.

"Mary," said Joseph, "this is Simeon, of Jerusalem."

The old man took the sleeping child from the mother's arms and gazed upon his face. Then he looked upward and praised God, saying, "Lord, now lettest thou thy servant depart in peace, according to thy word, for mine eyes have seen thy salvation."

Mary and Joseph listened quietly to the words of Simeon.

18

The child Jesus, brought to the temple to be presented to the Lord, is recognized by Simeon as the Saviour.

© Providence Lithograph Company

Having seen his star in the East, three wise men journey to Jerusalem, and inquire for him who is born King of the Jews.

TO HUMBLE SHEPHERDS of Bethlehem and to a devout old man of Jerusalem the birth of Jesus had been announced. Meantime, far to the east, three other men had reason to believe that the long-awaited King of the Jews had been born. These men were not of humble position. They were magi, or scholars, who studied the stars. When they found a new star in the sky, they believed it heralded the birth, somewhere in the world, of one who would become great.

The star they had just discovered in the eastern sky was bright indeed. One of the three magi had seen it from China, another from Persia, another from India. They were not Jews, but they were familiar with the Jewish Scriptures. Could this glowing star be the "star out of Jacob" that Balaam, the soothsayer, had foretold many centuries ago? The three magi agreed to follow it and see. If a new king had appeared, they would be among the first to acclaim him.

Westward the three men rode their camels, over the long caravan route to Damascus, the great market place of the world. Then they went south, through Galilee, Samaria, and into Judea.

"We will find the king we seek in Jerusalem," they said. "Jerusalem was the capital city of the great King David."

When the magi reached Jerusalem they asked, "Where is he that is born King of the Jews? We have seen his star in the east, and are come to worship him."

The Roman soldier at the city gate laughed. The priests in the temple scoffed, saying, "We would have been the first to hear."

But the glowing star beckoned the magi on.

When they saw the star, they rejoiced with exceeding great joy

A FEW MILES south of Jerusalem, the star suddenly became fixed in its course, shining directly over Bethlehem. And when the magi saw this, they rejoiced with exceeding great joy. Impatiently, they prodded their camels up to the city gate. They had come far, but perhaps their long quest was ended.

As the three magi rode through the market place, tradesmen and shoppers stopped their bargaining to stare. They did not often see travelers from the East, for Bethlehem was not on a caravan route. They watched curiously as the strangers moved slowly toward the home of Joseph, the new carpenter. They wondered who these richly dressed men could be, and what might be their business with the carpenter.

Joseph looked up from his workbench as the magi stopped before his door. Were these more visitors to the cradle of the little son? What hospitality could his humble home offer them?

"Mary," he called to his wife. Mary would know what to do. Often he marveled at her wisdom.

Courteously, the three magi greeted Joseph, who gave them water to wash the dust from their feet. Then they entered the tiny home, where Mary sat holding the baby Jesus.

The young mother sat quietly as the magi worshiped the little child and opened the treasures they had brought to him. One presented gold for a king; another frankincense for the Son of God; and the third, myrrh for one who would know great sorrow.

22

The wise men arrive at Bethlehem, and worship the child, presenting him with kingly gifts.

Warned by God in a dream, Joseph takes the child with his mother into Egypt.

24

Take the child and his mother, and flee into Egypt

IN JERUSALEM, where the magi had stopped to inquire for a newly born king, the aged and evil King Herod was alarmed. Was somebody challenging the right of the Herods to rule Judea? "Go and search diligently for the young child," he had told the wise men, "and bring me word, that I may come and worship him also." But the wise men were warned by God of Herod's trickery, and they returned home by another way.

And not long after the magi's visit, Joseph awoke one night from a troubled sleep. "Mary, God spoke to me in a dream, saying, 'Arise, and take the young child and his mother, and flee into Egypt.' We must leave Bethlehem at once, tonight."

Mary quickly gathered some household goods for Joseph to pack on the little donkey. God had spoken to Joseph and she must obey. She did not question the ways of God.

Silently, Joseph led the donkey through the darkness down the southern slope of the city. Beside him, Mary carried the baby.

"When Herod dies, we will return," Joseph said, as they hurried along the caravan route to Egypt.

But Mary and Joseph never returned to Bethlehem. When King Herod died, his equally cruel son, Archelaus, became king of Judea. God directed Joseph to take the young wife and child back to their first home in Nazareth, which lay in Galilee.

And Mary was glad, for in Galilee there were green fields for a growing boy to explore and gentle hills to climb.

And the child grew,
and the grace of God was upon him

THE SPRING RAINS were over, and the hills outside Nazareth were aflame with color. Poppies and phlox and lupine waved in the warm sun. Inside the synagogue, a circle of small boys sat cross-legged on the floor, droning after the master the words of the lesson. Over and over they repeated the words of the Law until they could recite them without faltering. If they learned to read well, and knew the Law, they could read the lessons in the synagogue services when they grew up. That was the hope of their humble parents. But today, when everything outside called to play, the Law was a dreary business.

At last the master rolled up the scroll. The lesson was over. Bidding his teacher a hasty good-by, Jesus ran swiftly down the street toward home. If Mother had not gone to the well, he could take his own water jug and go with her. Then perhaps they could climb their favorite hillside outside the city. There were wonderful things to be seen from that hillside. Sometimes a company of Roman soldiers marched stiffly downhill on their way to Jerusalem, standards held aloft, swords and shields glistening. Or there might be a long camel train of merchants from far countries moving slowly along the winding road. To the west, the shining waters of the Sea of Galilee were dotted with sailboats, and to the north the peaks of Herod's beautiful palace pushed up into the blue sky.

Jesus ran faster. Every minute of the day was precious, for life in the busy town of Nazareth in Galilee was full of wonders and delights for a lad of ten. And he grew, and waxed strong, filled with wisdom: and the grace of God was upon him.

The childhood of Jesus is spent in Nazareth, the grace of God being with him.

Jesus goes up with his parents to the Passover at the age of twelve years and tarries behind in the temple.

I must be about my Father's business

THE ROAD that led south to Jerusalem was thronged with pilgrims going to the holy city to celebrate the Passover. Joseph and Mary and Jesus were among them. It was a merry pilgrimage. Jesus raced excitedly on ahead with his friends, or led the little donkey and dreamed of the wonderful temple at Jerusalem that he was soon to see.

Up ahead a group of pilgrims started to chant, and one by one others picked up the song. Jesus joined them and marched proudly to the rhythm. *Our feet shall stand within thy gates, O Jerusalem, whither the tribes go up.*

At the end of the fourth day of their journey, Jesus and Mary and Joseph entered the city of Jerusalem, just as the priests were calling the people to worship with long blasts from their silver trumpets. For eight days the Passover Festival continued. On the morning after its close, when they were ready to start for home, Mary and Joseph could not find Jesus.

"He has gone ahead with his friends," Mary said.

But when Jesus had not appeared at the end of the day, they returned to Jerusalem to look for him.

For three days they searched the city. Finally they went to the temple, and there was Jesus, listening closely to the lectures of the teachers and asking questions that amazed the learned men.

Gently, Mary chided her son. "Thy father and I have sought thee sorrowing," she said.

"How is it that ye sought me?" Jesus answered. "Wist ye not that I must be about my Father's business?"

And Jesus increased in wisdom and stature

AT HOME in Nazareth, Jesus did not forget the experience he had had in Jerusalem. As he sat with his classmates in the synagogue, he remembered his talks with the teachers in the temple. Some day he would talk with them again and learn more about the meaning of these words of the Law he was repeating.

Every Jewish boy was required by the ancient Law of Moses to learn a trade, to work with his hands, even though he might some day be a learned rabbi or great scholar. There were many rabbis who were skillful woodcutters or tentmakers. But Jesus, the son of a poor carpenter, must learn a trade of necessity, for there would be no money for further education.

So, each day after school, Jesus worked with Joseph at his carpenter's bench and learned to shape harness poles and goads and to build sturdy beds and chests and kneading troughs. Some day, when there was time, Joseph promised, they would build a boat that Jesus could row on the stream nearby.

So Jesus increased in wisdom and stature, and in favor with God and men. Often Mary paused at her work to watch her husband and her son. Jesus was happy at the workbench, and earnest, too. Sometimes, when he looked up at her gravely, she recalled the words of Simeon on that day so long ago when she had dedicated her infant son to God: "This child is set for the fall and rising of many in Israel, that thoughts out of many hearts may be revealed."

Was this eager, active boy to be the leader of his people? Mary spoke to no one about these things, but she pondered them in her heart.

He returns with his parents to Nazareth where he is subject to them.

Jesus is baptized in the Jordan by John the Baptist who sees the Spirit of God descend upon him.

Thou art my beloved Son, in whom I am well pleased

THREE MONTHS before Jesus was born, Mary's cousin, Elisabeth, had given birth to a son whom Zacharias, his father, had named John. The two young cousins, so nearly of an age, grew to manhood, Jesus in a humble carpenter's home in Galilee, John in the comfortable household of a priest of the temple in Jerusalem.

"And thou, child, shall go before the Lord to prepare his ways," John's aged father had prophesied.

And so it proved to be. As a young man, John preferred the solitude of the rugged wilderness to the comforts of his father's priestly calling. He spent long hours studying and thinking about the Scriptures. In time, he set out on a preaching mission, foretelling the appearance of a Messiah.

"Prepare ye the way of the Lord," he cried to the people who came to hear him preach. "Make straight in the wilderness a highway for our God." And many people believed John's prophecy and became his disciples.

On a winter day, as John was baptizing new converts at the ford of Bethabarah on the Jordan River, he saw Jesus approaching.

"I, too, wish to be baptized," Jesus said to John.

"I have need to be baptized of thee, and comest thou to me?" John asked humbly.

"Suffer it to be so," Jesus answered him.

Then John baptized Jesus, and as Jesus went up out of the water, the Spirit of God descended upon him like a dove, and a voice from heaven said, "This is my beloved Son, in whom I am well pleased."

Then was Jesus led into the wilderness

THE BAPTISM of Jesus had shown John's followers that Jesus, too, was a believer in John's message that the Messiah was at hand. The people who saw the baptism did not know that Jesus was the Messiah. But Jesus had heard God's voice saying, "This is my beloved Son," and he knew that he must begin his mission.

This was the end of his quiet life as a carpenter in Nazareth. He must be separated from home and family. He must give his entire life to bringing the will of God to his people, as the prophets of Israel had done before him.

What was God's will for his own life? How was he to begin his mission? How was he to interpret God to people who were looking for a Messiah who would free them from Rome?

Jesus had many questions to be answered, and only God could guide him. He must be alone, far from the busy world of Palestine, to commune with his Father.

So it was that Jesus was led up of the Spirit into the wilderness. Slowly, he climbed the rocky path that led toward the chalk-white cliffs of a high, bleak mountain. As he climbed, the path became rougher and the land more barren.

Night was coming on, and a chill wind from the hills pierced Jesus' thin garment. But his step was firm as he followed the steep path, and his spirits were high. God was leading him to this place. He would pray to God, whose "beloved Son" he was, and wait for the Father's answer. But it was not the voice of God that Jesus was to hear on the top of the barren mountain.

The Spirit drives Jesus into the wilderness.

35

In the wilderness, Jesus fasts forty days and forty nights, being tempted by Satan.

*And he was in
the wilderness forty days*

THE SUMMIT of the mountain was a wild and lonely place of ragged cliffs, jagged rocks, and dry sand. Eagles circled overhead, and wild beasts crept down during the night hours to drink from the water that swept through the gorge in the rocks.

Jesus came to the end of the steep path and climbed over the rocks toward the summit of the mountain. He looked down over the gray cliffs below. How far was this lonely wilderness from the green hills of Galilee! A sudden longing for the friendly warmth of home came over him.

The day passed, followed by a dreary night. Much of his vigil was spent in prayer, but he could hear no response from God. His loneliness and longing for home increased. Small doubts grew larger, and his courage began to weaken. Had he made a mistake? Would God reveal himself in this lonely place?

He became hungry, and the rocks at his feet reminded him of the small loaves of bread they ate at home. Fascinated, he fixed his gaze upon them. And suddenly he heard a voice.

"If thou be the Son of God, command that these stones be made bread."

This was not God's voice. This was the voice of the evil one.

Jesus answered the tempter firmly. "It is written, man shall not live by bread alone."

He was the Son of God, but he would not use his power for physical comfort. That could be left in God's hands. But the tempter was not so easily put aside.

WITH GREAT CUNNING, the tempter approached Jesus again.

"If thou be the Son of God, cast thyself down: for it is written, 'He shall give his angels charge concerning thee: and in their hands they shall bear thee up, lest thou dash thy foot against a stone.' "

But Jesus answered, "It is written again, 'Thou shalt not tempt the Lord thy God.' "

And still the tempter tried to break his will. Leading him to a high peak, he pointed out the kingdoms of the world that lay below and said, "All these things will I give thee, if thou wilt fall down and worship me."

For many days Jesus struggled with himself and with the spirit of evil that tempted him to forsake God and place his trust in Satan. But day after day the Holy Spirit within him grew stronger. Through his temptations he discovered God's will. The Kingdom of God was not to be built through power or wealth or other material things, but through love and service and the slow, lasting ways of God.

"Get thee hence, Satan," Jesus commanded the evil one. "For it is written, 'Thou shalt worship the Lord thy God, and him only shalt thou serve.' Then the evil one left him, and Jesus stood triumphant on the mountain peak, and angels came and ministered to his needs.

Master of his own soul, confident that he could carry out God's will, Jesus strode down the rocky path, back to the people he must serve.

38

The temptation being ended, Satan leaves Jesus.

Jesus then returns to the Jordan where John and Andrew follow him, the latter bringing also his brother Simon.

We have found the Messiah!

JOHN AND two of his disciples were standing on the bank of the Jordan River. As they talked, Jesus approached, and John saw him and exclaimed, "Behold the Lamb of God!"

Startled, the two disciples looked at each other. Could this Jesus be the Messiah? If he was, they must talk to him. So they followed Jesus as he continued along the river path.

Turning, Jesus spoke to the two men. "What seek ye?"

Their answer was another question. "Rabbi, where abidest thou?"

"Come, and ye shall see," Jesus replied, and the two men went with him to his tent nearby.

They talked together far into the night, and when the dawn was breaking one of the men, Andrew, a fisherman from Galilee, rushed home to find his brother.

"Simon! Simon! We have found the Messiah!" he announced. "Come quickly. I will take thee to him!"

Simon scarcely dared to believe the wonderful news. Had the Messiah really come? Could Andrew have talked with him?

Back along the road to the river the two brothers hastened. When Jesus met them, he looked into Simon's eager, earnest face. Here was the strength he needed to help build his Kingdom. It was usual for a Galilean to take a new name when a change came into his life, and now Jesus had a new name for Simon.

"Thou art Simon, the son of John," Jesus said. "Thou shalt be called Peter, which is by interpretation a rock."

With Peter and Andrew and two other disciples, Philip and Nathanael, Jesus journeys into Galilee.

Jesus attends a marriage feast in Cana, and there performs his first miracle.

A WEDDING CELEBRATION was taking place in Cana. The bride and groom were friends of Jesus, and he and some of his disciples were among the guests. Yesterday they had watched as the bride was carried to her new home in a chair borne by the groom. The ceremony of breaking the ritual vase had been performed, and the bride had lifted her veil. Feasting and merrymaking had been going on for two days. Quantities of food had been consumed, and the wine had been blessed by the rabbi.

"Blessed be the Creator of the fruit of the trees," he had prayed.

Talking with friends, Jesus saw his mother coming toward him. She was concerned about something. "They have no more wine," she said to Jesus.

Jesus read her thoughts. "The time has not yet come for me to reveal my powers," he said to her.

But Mary would not be put off. Their kind hosts were embarrassed, and Jesus could help.

"Whatsoever he saith unto you, do it," she said to the servants.

"Fill the waterpots with water," Jesus ordered.

The servants filled the pots to the brim.

"Now draw it out and bear it to the ruler of the feast."

The ruler tasted the rich wine that had come from the waterpots. He turned to the bridegroom. "Every man serves the best wine first. Thou hast kept the good wine until now."

The bridegroom was puzzled, but Mary smiled happily, and Philip and Nathanael nodded. Their Master had performed a miracle.

45

Make not my Father's house a house of merchandise

FROM ALL OVER the Mediterranean world, faithful Jews were coming to Jerusalem for the Passover. From Babylonia, Egypt, and Asia Minor they came, to attend the eight-day festival.

During the Passover periods of sacrificing, the huge Court of the Gentiles was filled with people. In the booths set up around the walls, the temple priests sold doves and lambs and cattle to be sacrificed on the altar fires. Here the money-changers exchanged the foreign money of pilgrims from other countries for the coins with which sacrificial purchases must be made. Here the Levites, the attendants at the temple, sold salt and flour and oil for temple offerings.

Jesus, as was his custom, came down to Jerusalem for the Passover. As he entered the magnificent temple, shrill arguments between buyers and sellers of cattle, the clanging of silver coins, and quarreling among the merchants met his ears.

Quickly he knotted some cords into a scourge. Then, striding across the great court, he overturned the tables of the money-changers, and snapping the scourge, he drove the cattle out of the court.

"Take these things hence!" he cried. And to the sellers of sacrificial doves, "Make not my Father's house a house of merchandise!"

The priests were angry, but they made little protest. The money-changers scrambled to recover the coins, but they were silent. Some among them were shamed and penitent. They knew that this rabbi from Galilee spoke truthfully. Had not the prophet Malachi written, "I will send my messenger, and the Lord shall suddenly come to his temple and he shall purify the sons of Levi and purge them"?

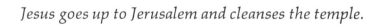

Jesus goes up to Jerusalem and cleanses the temple.

47

Nicodemus, a ruler of the Jews, comes to Jesus by night to be further informed concerning his doctrine.

Except a man be born anew, he cannot see the Kingdom of God

ONE EVENING when Jesus was resting on the cool roof of John's home in Jerusalem, a man came up the steps from the silent street below. He wore the silken mantle of the wealthy, and when he spoke his voice was cultured and flattering.

"Rabbi," he began, "we know that thou art a teacher come from God: for no man can do these signs that thou doest, except God be with him."

The name of Jesus' caller was Nicodemus. He was a member of the powerful Sanhedrin, the religious court of the Jewish people, and he was an important person in Jerusalem. Nicodemus had heard of Jesus and was interested in his message. He knew that many of the things this rabbi preached echoed the words of the prophets. Could he be the Messiah? To satisfy himself, Nicodemus decided to have a talk with Jesus. But not wanting his friends to know, he called on Jesus after nightfall.

As Nicodemus talked, Jesus sensed the unspoken questions of his timid caller. What is the Kingdom of God? How do I enter?

Overhead the stars twinkled in a purple sky. A soft breeze touched the garments of the two men as they talked long and earnestly together.

"Except a man be born anew, Nicodemus, he cannot see the Kingdom of God," Jesus said.

Nicodemus could not understand. What was this rebirth? "How can a man be born when he is old?" he asked Jesus.

Again Jesus told him, "Except a man be born of water and the Spirit, he cannot enter into the Kingdom."

Whosoever drinketh of the water that I give him shall not thirst

THE SHORTEST, most direct route from Judea to Galilee began at Jerusalem and went north through the hills. But few Judeans ever took that route, for it passed through Samaria. Jews and Samaritans despised one another. To speak to a Samaritan was unthinkable to a pious Jew, for the Samaritans were a mixed race; because of this, they were considered "unclean."

Jesus was preparing to return to Galilee from Judea. Despite the mild protest of the disciples who were to accompany him, he chose to travel the cooler hill road through Samaria.

About noon of the second day, Jesus and his companions reached Sychar, the ancient city of Jacob, in Samaria. Preferring to eat in the hills rather than in an unfriendly town, the disciples went into the city to buy bread and fruit. Jesus sat down by Jacob's Well to rest. As he waited, a woman from the city approached the well. Her dark eyes flashed a bold look in Jesus' direction and then looked quickly away.

Jesus was thirsty and had no jug. "Give me to drink," he said to the woman.

Surprised, the woman turned to him. "How is it that thou, being a Jew, askest drink of me, which am a Samaritan woman?"

"If thou knewest the gift of God, and who it is that saith to thee, 'Give me to drink,' thou wouldst have asked of him, and he would have given thee living water," was Jesus' astonishing reply.

For a long time, the woman listened to Jesus. Then she hastened back to the city. "Come," she urged her neighbors, "and see a man who hath told me all things. Is not he the Christ?"

Journeying northward through Samaria, Jesus rests by Jacob's Well,
and reveals who he is to a woman of the country.

51

His teaching is rejected with fury by his own townsfolk of Nazareth, and he is thrust forth from the synagogue and from the city.

Today has this Scripture been fulfilled in your ears

THE SERVICE in the synagogue at Nazareth had been, as usual, a long one. Some heads were beginning to nod drowsily when Jesus, invited by the ruler of the synagogue to be the speaker of the day, began to read from the prophet Isaiah:

The Spirit of the Lord is upon me,
Because he anointed me to preach good tidings to the poor:
He hath sent me to proclaim release to the captives,
And recovering of sight to the blind,
To set at liberty them that are bruised,
To proclaim the acceptable year of the Lord.

He reads well, the older people said to themselves, this son of Joseph who had grown up in their city.

Then Jesus sat down, as was the custom, to comment on the Scriptures he had read.

"Today hath this Scripture been fulfilled in your ears," he began. "God hath appointed me to preach good tidings, to proclaim release for those captive in sin, to proclaim the acceptable year of the Lord."

The expressions of the faces of his audience turned from astonishment to anger. Was not this Jesus, the carpenter's son? He had grown up with their own boys. How dare he make such claims for himself? They would deal with this young blasphemer. Surging forward to the front, they pushed and dragged Jesus out of the synagogue and through the streets to the place of execution outside the city walls.

"Stone him!" the mob cried. But some force they could not understand held them back, and Jesus slipped quietly away.

TO BE EJECTED from the synagogue where he had worshiped with his parents and gone to school with his childhood friends had been a sad experience for Jesus. But peace returned to his spirit as he walked down the green slopes and across the plain from Nazareth to Capernaum, on the Sea of Galilee.

Approaching the city, he could see the white limestone of the synagogue standing out against the flat, dark roofs around it. Within the city it was hot, and an odor of fish from the lakefront mingled with the sweet fragrance of orange blossoms from many gardens.

Jesus knew that the synagogue was the natural place for him to preach his Gospel. He would try again. So on the Sabbath Day he went to the synagogue in Capernaum and taught. Unlike the people of Nazareth, those who heard Jesus in Capernaum listened with interest. They saw that he spoke with authority.

But there were many in Capernaum who had heard more exciting things about Jesus. His fame had spread abroad throughout all Galilee. He had turned water into wine up in Cana, it was said, and that very morning, in the synagogue in Capernaum, he had cast devils out of a man. At evening, when the sun was set and Jesus was returning to his lodgings, they brought to him the sick, the lame, the blind, and those that were possessed of evil spirits.

Jesus turned no one away. As he spoke gently to some and firmly to others, and laid his hands on fevered brows and crippled limbs, the power of God flowed from him to heal and to bless. And all the city were gathered together to see him, and he healed many that were sick.

54

© Providence Lithograph Company

The Sabbath being ended, the people of Capernaum bring to him
many afflicted with disease, and he heals them.

55

© 1957 Providence Lithograph Company

Because of the pressure of the multitude, Jesus seats himself in Peter's fishing boat, and teaches the people many things by parables.

He that hath ears to hear, let him hear

I T WAS early evening and Jesus had gone down to the shore of the Sea of Galilee to rest. But so great a multitude of people followed him that he stepped into Peter's boat. Now he could see them all and they could see him as he stood at the bow of the boat.

Jesus looked at the faces turned toward him, expectantly waiting. Here were the scoffers, the curious, the honest doubters, and the few who had accepted his Gospel. What could he say that would reach them all? How could he explain the Kingdom of God so that all of them would understand? He decided to tell them a story.

There was no breeze tonight. The palm and oleander trees around the lake seemed to listen, too, as Jesus described a scene familiar to his audience.

"Behold, there went out a sower to sow." They could see the sower, striding across his land, taking large handfuls of seed from the basket at his waist and casting the seed to the right and left in wide sweeps.

"And as he sowed, some fell by the wayside." Yes, the audience nodded. That always happened, and the birds had a feast. "And some fell on stony ground, where it had not much earth; and because it had no root, it withered away. And some fell among thorns, and the thorns grew up and choked it." This was all too true. Such a wasteful way of planting was the only one they knew. "And others fell on good ground and did yield fruit that sprang up and increased."

When some of his hearers questioned Jesus about the meaning of the story, he said, "The sower soweth the Word. The ground is the hearts and minds of men. He that hath ears to hear, let him hear."

SIMON PETER was tired and discouraged. He and his brother had been out in their boat all night and had caught nothing. They had sailed from one fishing ground to another. They had tapped the sides of the boat to frighten the fish into the nets, but that had not helped. Finally, at dawn, they had rowed back across the misty lake and gone home to sleep.

Now, early in the evening, Peter sat in his boat as Jesus, standing in the bow, told the multitudes on the shore the story of the sower.

When Jesus had finished speaking, he turned to Peter and said, "Launch out into the deep and let down your nets for a draught."

"Master, we have toiled all the night, and have taken nothing," Peter replied. "Nevertheless, at thy word I will let down the nets."

Strong arms pulled the boat out into deep water and let the big net down over the side. The weights in the net carried it toward the bottom. Immediately, it began to fill. No fisherman had ever had a catch like this. Perch, carp, and pike strained the net until it began to break and Peter had to call to men in another boat to help him pull in. The catch filled both boats to overflowing.

The astonished fishermen rowed the boats back to the shore, where Jesus stood waiting. Peter rushed to kneel at his feet.

"Depart from me; for I am a sinful man, O Lord," he cried.

Jesus motioned the fearful disciple to stand up. "It is men we need and who need us, Peter," he said. "Fear not; from henceforth, thou shalt be a fisher of men."

And they forsook their boats, and followed him.

©Providence Lithograph Company

The preaching ended, Jesus commands Simon Peter to let down his net in deep water, and a great number of fishes are caught.

59

Providence Lithograph Company

Passing the customs bench, Jesus commands Levi, the publican, to follow him.

*And he forsook all,
rose up, and followed him*

THE GATE through which travelers entered the city of Capernaum from the lake was a busy place. Here merchants and visitors were stopped by the customs officers, the publicans who collected duty on all goods brought into the city.

Jesus walked up the ramp from the lake and through the gate on a day when a wealthy publican named Levi was on duty. Jesus had no goods to be taxed, but he stopped at the customs bench, his eyes fixed upon Levi. Here was a man who might be called away from his selfish life, to become the kind of man God intended him to be.

"Levi," Jesus said, "I am the Messiah foretold by the prophets. I need your help in building God's kingdom. Follow me, Levi."

Astonished, Levi half rose to his feet to look into the face of Jesus. And he forsook all, and rose up, and followed Jesus.

The publicans were considered "sinners" and were held in contempt by the Jewish people. Although they were Jews, they collected taxes for Rome, and they were looked upon as collaborators with the conqueror. They were disliked for another reason, too. Anything they could collect over and above the percentage claimed by the Roman government, they could keep. As a result, fraud and dishonesty were common among them.

When the grateful Levi made a feast in his home and invited Jesus and his disciples, Jesus' enemies murmured against him. "Why do ye eat and drink with publicans and sinners?" they asked.

Jesus' answer silenced them. "I came not to call the righteous, but sinners to repentance."

Blessed are ye poor: for yours is the Kingdom of God

ONE DAY JESUS left the city and its crowds and went out to a mountainside to pray. When he came down from the mountain the following day, he had made a decision. He must have helpers to assist him in building the Kingdom of God.

Jesus chose twelve men from among the people who had accepted him and become his followers. These twelve were to be his special disciples. They would leave their homes and go with him to be trained for carrying on his work. Some of them had already been accompanying him. The names of the twelve disciples were Peter, Andrew, James, John, Philip, Nathanael, Levi, Thomas, James the son of Alphaeus, Simon the Zealot, Judas the son of James, and Judas Iscariot.

Jesus and his disciples were talking together one day on a hillside outside Capernaum, near the lake. Others of his followers joined them, until, by the afternoon, there was a great multitude. While the crowd listened, Jesus spoke directly to his followers, telling them of the rejection they would often experience here on earth and the virtues they must possess if they would enter the Kingdom of Heaven.

Standing on the mount, Jesus said, "Blessed are ye poor: for yours is the Kingdom of God. Blessed are ye that hunger now: for ye shall be filled. Blessed are ye that weep now: for ye shall laugh. Blessed are ye when men shall hate you and reproach you, and cast out your name as evil, for the Son of Man's sake. Rejoice, for behold your reward is great in heaven: for in the same manner did their fathers unto the prophets."

And the crowds of people surged forth, trying to touch Jesus, and power came from him and he healed them.

62

Jesus goes up into a mountain, whither he is followed by his disciples. From these he selects twelve to be his apostles.

63

Jesus comes down the mountain and, meeting a leper, he cleanses him.

Lord, if thou wilt, thou canst make me clean

I T HAD BEEN many years since the man named Isaac had seen his family, except from a long distance. One morning, years ago, he had awakened to find terrifying patches of white on his hands and arms. He knew what that meant. He was sick with the dread disease of leprosy. And, under the law, he must be banished from society.

Today he had come down from his cave shelter in the hills to beg for food. Crying "Unclean, unclean," to warn of his approach, he neared the city gate. A crowd of people who were coming through the gate seemed to be in a happy mood. Perhaps they would be generous. Pulling his ragged garment about his thin body, Isaac limped closer. The people who saw him backed hurriedly away, but they did not shout and wave him off as they had done before. And then Isaac saw a white-robed figure whom the crowd was following. Could this be a prophet? Was there help here for an outcast? Timidly, Isaac crept nearer.

"Lord." His feeble voice could scarcely be heard. But the prophet heard, and held out his hand to this pitiful man whom others shunned.

Courage and faith flowed through Isaac's heart.

"Lord, if thou wilt, thou canst make me clean."

Tears flowed from the sick man's eyes as Jesus touched his hands.

"I will," Jesus said. "Be thou made clean." And at once the leprosy was cleansed.

"Go thy way, Isaac," Jesus commanded him. "Show thyself to the priest, and offer the gift that Moses commanded."

His heart filled with gratitude, Isaac went down to the temple to make his offering.

As thou hast believed, so be it done unto thee

THE CENTURION commanding the Roman guard at the military post in Capernaum was different from most of the proud, unfriendly Roman officers in Palestine. He had made friends with the people and had presented the city with a fine synagogue.

One day as Jesus was passing through the city gate, the centurion approached him. He had heard Jesus speak and knew of his power. "Lord, my servant lieth in the house sick of the palsy, grievously tormented."

"I will come and heal him," Jesus promised.

The centurion had not become a follower of Jesus, nor a member of the Jewish religious community, but he had seen enough of Jesus' works to have faith in him.

"Lord, I am not worthy that thou shouldst come under my roof," he said. "But only say the word, and my servant will be healed."

The centurion was accustomed to giving orders and having them carried out. But he was humble in the presence of Jesus.

"I also am a man under authority," he said to Jesus, "having under myself soldiers: and I say to this one, 'Go,' and he goeth; and to another, 'Come,' and he cometh; and to my servant, 'Do this,' and he doeth it."

Jesus marveled at the centurion's humility and faith. Turning to his disciples who had been standing near, Jesus said, "I have not found so great faith, no, not in Israel."

To the powerful officer who had pleaded in humility for his servant, Jesus said, "Go thy way; as thou hast believed, so be it done unto thee."

As Jesus enters into Capernaum, there comes to him a centurion, who beseeches him to heal his servant stricken with palsy.

67

©1957 Providence Lithograph Company

At the approach to a city called Nain, he raises from the dead a young man, the only son of his mother, a widow.

68

THE VILLAGE of Nain perched on the northern slope of the mountain, "Little Hermon," a few miles from Nazareth. Nain was a small, unimportant village, located away from the busy highway that led south to Samaria and on to Jerusalem. Often in his boyhood Jesus had looked south from a hillside of Nazareth, across the Valley of Jezreel, to Nain. The Valley of Jezreel was rich in the history of his people. Here, not far from Nain, King Ahab and his evil Queen Jezebel had owned a royal residence, and here the prophet Elijah had dared to accuse King Ahab of the murder of Nahob, whose vineyards the king wanted for himself.

One day Jesus and his disciples were climbing the footpath that led up the mountain to the village. As they approached the gate of Nain, they met a small funeral procession coming out. Behind the hired mourners and flute players, a young widow walked beside the bier of her only son. She wept quietly and hopelessly.

"Only a funeral procession," said the disciples, as they stepped aside to let it pass. But Jesus looked with compassion upon the mourning mother, even though she neither knew him nor asked anything of him.

"Weep not," he said to her, as he came nearer and touched the bier.

"Young man, I say unto thee, Arise," Jesus commanded.

And he that was dead sat up, and began to speak.

Fear took hold of the mourners and the flute players and the villagers who stood about. Then they glorified God saying, "A great prophet is arisen among us: and God hath visited his people."

IMON WAS A member of the sect called Pharisees. They were students and teachers of the Law who criticized Jesus because he broke the Law when it made life hard for the common people. Simon, a wealthy and devout Jew, did not believe that Jesus was the Messiah. But, perhaps out of curiosity, he invited Jesus to dine with him. He did not give Jesus water to wash his feet, or anoint his guest's head with oil, as was the custom. Jesus ignored the discourtesies, and joined the other guests, reclining on the couch at Simon's table.

Then suddenly and silently a woman came into Simon's beautiful dining court. Although a Jewish home was easily entered and the dining area of a wealthy home was almost a public place, this visitor was not welcome. Before Simon could have her sent away, she began to anoint the feet of Jesus with perfume and wipe them with her hair.

Simon looked at Jesus with scorn. Any true prophet would know that this woman was a sinner, but this man calmly accepted the weeping woman's attentions.

Jesus knew what Simon was thinking, and said, "Simon, I have something to say unto thee:

"A certain lender had two debtors: the one owed five hundred pence, and the other fifty. Neither could pay, and he forgave them both. Which of them will love him most?"

There was only one answer that Simon could give. "He, I suppose, to whom he forgave the most."

Then Jesus turned to the woman and said, "Thy faith hath saved thee; go in peace."

70

At the house of Simon the Pharisee, he forgives a sinful woman.

Crossing the Sea of Galilee with his disciples, Jesus stills a tempest which had arisen.

MANY OF JESUS' disciples were fishermen, and often Jesus went out with Peter, Andrew, James, and John on the Sea of Galilee. Only there could Jesus rest undisturbed.

One day he climbed into Peter's boat as it lay on the beach near Capernaum. "Let us go over unto the other side of the lake," he said.

There was a brisk breeze blowing as they started out. Jesus lifted his face to the fresh, cool air and then, resting on a pillow at the prow of the boat, he fell asleep.

Suddenly the disciples saw dark clouds rushing across the sky. These expert fishermen knew that winds sometimes swept down quickly from the hills and caused violent storms on the shallow lake. Before they had time to reef the sail, the storm broke. Huge waves pounded the boat, and the craft was in danger of sinking.

"Master! Master! We perish," the disciples cried to Jesus.

Jesus awoke and rose to his feet, steadying himself against the wind. Then he stretched forth his hand over the raging sea. At once the wind ceased blowing and the sea became calm.

"Where is your faith?" he asked the disciples.

The fishermen looked at the calm waters that only a few seconds before had been threatening their boat and their lives. They were astonished and fearful of the power of their Master. "Who then is this," they said among themselves, "that he commandeth even the winds and the water, and they obey him?"

Silently, they unfurled the sail and continued toward the eastern shore of the still and peaceful sea.

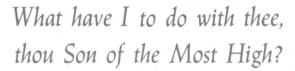

What have I to do with thee, thou Son of the Most High?

J ESUS AND his disciples went ashore on the eastern side of the lake, and some of the disciples built a fire. They would dry their wet clothes and prepare something to eat.

The cliffs that rose sharply from the shore were honeycombed with caves. As Jesus walked along the rocky path below the cliffs, horrible sounds broke out from somewhere above him. The disciples on the shore looked up in alarm as a naked, screaming man dashed down over the rocks and knelt before Jesus.

"What have I to do with thee, Jesus, thou Son of the Most High God?" he cried.

The disciples rushed up the path to rescue the Master. They saw the broken fetters that dangled from the man's ankles. He must be one of those prisoners whom the keepers could not handle and so drove up into the hills.

As Jesus talked calmly to the tormented man, he seemed to be battling with evil spirits within his wretched body.

"Come out of the man," Jesus commanded.

And the devils came out of the man and he became quiet.

"What is thy name?" Jesus asked him.

"Legion," the man replied, for a legion of devils had possessed him.

Nearby, some farmers were feeding their swine. When they saw that this wild man whom they had long feared had become quiet, they rushed into the city to tell what had come to pass.

Immediately crowds rushed out of the city to see for themselves. And they saw the man, now in his right mind, sitting with Jesus.

74

In the country of the Gadarenes, Jesus is met by a demoniac from whom he casts out a legion of devils.

© 1957 Providence Lithograph Company

A paralytic man, because of the crowd, is let down through a roof at Jesus' feet.

Arise, and take up thy bed

PETER LIVED in Capernaum, a city on the Sea of Galilee, and Peter's home became the headquarters of Jesus during his Galilean ministry. Here he always returned after preaching missions.

Today, Jesus had just come back to Capernaum after a few days spent in neighboring towns. He had not been home long before the word of his return spread. Immediately the people stormed Peter's small house to see and hear the new prophet.

Four men had brought a friend who was sick of the palsy to Peter's house, hoping that Jesus would cure him. Since they could not get into the house because of the crowd, they carried the sick man's cot up the outside stairway, made a hole in the soft mortar of the flat roof, and let the cot down into the room where Jesus sat. Seeing their faith in him, Jesus said to the sick man, "Son, thy sins are forgiven."

Some scribes were watching. When they heard the words of Jesus, they said angrily, "Why doth this man thus speak? He blasphemeth. Who can forgive sins but one, even God?"

Jesus answered their criticism with a question. "Is it easier to say to the sick man, 'Thy sins are forgiven,' or to say, 'Arise and take up thy bed, and walk'?"

Then he turned to the sick man and said, "Arise, take up thy bed, and go unto thy house."

And the sick man arose, picked up his bed, and walked out of the house. Now the scribes saw that Jesus not only forgave the man's sins, but healed him as well. And the people glorified God, saying, "We never saw it on this fashion."

Thy faith
hath made thee whole

JAIRUS, A MAN of importance in Capernaum, was the ruler of the synagogue. He had often given Jesus permission to speak there on the Sabbath Day and had been impressed by his words.

When Jairus' daughter became gravely ill, he came to Jesus for help.

"My little daughter is at the point of death," he said. "I pray thee, that thou come and lay thy hands on her, that she may be made whole, and live."

On his way to Jairus' home, Jesus was followed by a crowd of people. They pressed closely about him, but suddenly Jesus felt one touch that was different from the press of the crowd.

"Who touched my garments?" he asked.

The disciples were amused. "Thou seest the multitude thronging thee, and sayest thou, 'Who touched me?' "

But Jesus looked around, and a woman came from the crowd and knelt before him, trembling with fear.

"Rabbi," she said, "I had been ill for twelve years, and had suffered many things of many physicians, and was nothing bettered. But having heard of thee, I knew if I could but touch thy garment, I should be made whole. And thus it was. When I touched thy garment, I was healed."

At one side of the narrow street, merchants and customers bargained. Impatient tradesmen goaded their donkeys through the crowds blocking their way. Only the kneeling woman heard the quiet words of Jesus:

"Daughter, thy faith hath made thee whole; go in peace, and be whole of thy plague."

On the way to the house of Jairus, whose little daughter lies sick,
Jesus heals a woman in the crowd, and commends her faith.

At the house of Jairus, he finds the child dead and raises her.

JAIRUS WAITED patiently while Jesus spoke with the woman who had touched his garments in the crowded street. While Jesus was talking with her, servants came from Jairus' home to tell him that his daughter had died. Still the grief-stricken father did not leave, but waited to speak with Jesus.

"Why troublest thou the Master further?" someone asked.

But Jesus turned to the father with a word of hope. "Fear not," he said, "only believe." And taking Peter, James, and John with him, he accompanied Jairus back to his home.

As they approached the beautiful house they could hear loud sounds of mourning. The flutists were playing the lament, and hired mourners were wailing. Jesus motioned for them to stop.

"Why make ye a tumult, and weep? The child is not dead, but sleepeth."

The musicians and mourners laughed scornfully, and Jesus asked that they be sent from the house. Then he took the father and mother and entered the room where the body of the child lay. Touching her hand, he said, "Damsel, I say unto thee, Arise." And she rose up and walked.

Outside the house, the mourners waited, sure that they would be called back. They were amazed and fearful when the girl who had been dead walked from the house alive.

"Give her something to eat," Jesus commanded the happy parents, "and I charge thee to tell no man of this."

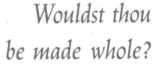
ONE OF THE entrances to the temple in Jerusalem, through which the animals for sacrifice were driven, was known as the Sheep Gate. Near this gate was a rectangular pool, surrounded by a colonnade of five porches. The source of the pool was a spring, which bubbled from time to time. The people believed that when it bubbled, the first person to bathe in it would become well. Consequently, the porches that surrounded the pool were always crowded with people who were ill and crippled.

Jesus had come down from Galilee to Jerusalem to celebrate the Feast of the Passover. Walking along the porches of the pool, he saw a lame man lying helplessly by. When Jesus learned that the man had been crippled for thirty-eight years, he said to him, "Wouldst thou be made whole?"

"Sir," the man replied, "I have no man, when the water is troubled, to put me into the pool: but while I am coming, another steppeth down before me."

"Arise, take up thy bed, and walk," Jesus said quietly to the astonished man.

And the man was made whole, and took up his bed and walked.

It was the Sabbath, and a bed was too heavy a load to be carried on the Sabbath, according to the Law. When some of the people said to the cured man, "It is not lawful for thee to carry thy bed," he could only reply, "He that made me whole, the same said unto me, 'Take up thy bed, and walk.' " But the man did not know who this was, for Jesus had disappeared in the crowd about the temple.

©Providence Lithograph Company

Jesus finds an infirm man at the Pool of Bethesda waiting to be healed by the troubling of the water; he bids him rise and walk.

83

Jesus, seeing the multitude of those he had taught, is moved by compassion, and miraculously feeds them.

84

Looking up to heaven, he blessed and broke the loaves

IT WAS early April, and the grass was fresh on the hills outside Capernaum. Jesus was tired. The crowds that followed him were so great that he had little time to rest, or even to eat.

"Come ye yourselves apart into a desert place, and rest awhile," he said one day to his disciples. So Andrew unmoored his boat and they set sail across the lake to a quiet place on the opposite shore.

But a few people standing about the quays at Capernaum saw them go and started to follow on foot around the shore. Word spread, and by the time Jesus and the disciples reached the other side, a large crowd had gathered there.

The disciples were annoyed, but Jesus said, "They are as sheep without a shepherd," and he began to teach them many things. When he had finished, the sun was beginning to set behind the hills.

"The day is far spent," the disciples said to Jesus, "and these people are far from home. Send them away, that they may buy themselves somewhat to eat."

"Give ye them to eat," was Jesus' astonishing reply.

"Shall we go and buy two hundred pennyworth of bread?" the disciples asked. Did Jesus not know that they had only five loaves of bread and two fishes?

"Ask them to sit on the grass in groups of fifty and one hundred," Jesus commanded. The puzzled disciples did as he asked. Then Jesus took the loaves and fishes, and looking up to heaven, he blessed and broke the loaves and told the disciples to distribute the food among the five thousand hungry people. And they all did eat and were filled.

Jesus, walking upon the sea, overtakes his disciples.

Be of good cheer. It is I

WHEN THE multitudes had been fed, Jesus sent them away. Then he asked the disciples to sail back across the lake without him. He wanted to go up into the mountain to pray in solitude.

The disciples got into their boat and set sail for the western shore and home. When evening came, and they were halfway across the lake, a strong westerly wind arose, driving the boat back in the opposite direction. It was useless to try to sail, so, taking turns at the oars, the men rowed against the wind. But at the fourth watch they were still far from the harbor.

Peter had just given up his place at the oars to James. As he stumbled toward the prow of the boat to rest, his weary glance caught sight of an apparition on the water ahead. It seemed to be the figure of a man, walking on the sea.

In terror, Peter called to his companions. Could they see the figure? Yes, they could see it, and they cried out, much troubled. What evil thing had befallen them, with the Master far away, alone on the land?

But the Master was not far away. As he walked toward them on the water he called, "Be of good cheer. It is I. Be not afraid."

Quickly the disciples helped Jesus into the boat. The wind ceased and the waters became calm and beautiful in the bright moonlight.

The disciples were amazed, and ashamed of their fear and lack of faith. They had not understood the feeding of the multitudes with the few loaves and fishes, and their hearts had been hardened so that they did not recognize their Master as he walked toward them on the sea.

O woman, great is thy faith

THE ENEMIES of Jesus were growing in numbers. Some of them plotted against his life, and to escape, he sometimes found it necessary to leave Galilee for a while.

On a spring morning, Jesus and the disciples started out on the highway that went west from Capernaum to the Phoenician city of Tyre. The fertile plains that spread outward from the hills of Phoenicia were dotted with orchards of lemon, apricot, fig, olive, and orange trees.

As they walked along, Jesus was reminded of his people's history. King David and King Solomon had purchased from the Phoenicians the cedars of Lebanon for building the temple and palace at Jerusalem.

After a three days' journey, Jesus and the disciples arrived at the home of some of their followers who lived in Tyre.

One day, as Jesus was leaving his friends' house, a Canaanite woman threw herself at his feet, crying, "Have mercy on me, O Lord, thou son of David; my daughter is grievously vexed with a devil!"

The disciples, who looked upon the woman as a foreigner, were annoyed that she should come to Jesus. "Send her away," they said.

Jesus rebuked them. "I was not sent but unto the lost sheep of the house of Israel."

To test the woman's faith, Jesus said to her, "It is not meet to take the children's bread and cast it to dogs."

"Yea, Lord," she answered humbly, "for even the dogs eat of the crumbs which fall from their master's table."

Jesus was satisfied. "O woman, great is thy faith; be it done unto thee even as thou wilt."

He tests the faith of a woman who comes to him on behalf of her daughter.

Thou art the Christ, the Son of the living God

FROM Tyre and Sidon Jesus returned for a brief time to Galilee, but again his enemies forced him to flee. This time Jesus went up the valley of the Jordan River to Caesarea Philippi. This city had been built by Philip, son of Herod the Great, during Jesus' boyhood. It was Philip's favorite residence and was named for him.

As Jesus approached the foothills, he lifted his face to the cool mountain air, sweetly scented by oleander and almond trees. Wild flowers carpeted the fields of the valley.

It was in this pagan territory, within sight of the shrines of two heathen cults, that the disciples made their first vows and stated their personal conviction that Jesus was the Son of God.

On one of their walks in the wooded hills, Jesus and the disciples stopped to rest in the shade of the oak and mulberry trees. Jesus was low in spirit. He had been rejected by most of his own people. Turning to the disciples, he asked, "Who do men say that the Son of Man is?"

"Some say John the Baptist; some Elijah; and others Jeremiah, or one of the prophets," the disciples told him.

Then came Jesus' question: "But who say ye that I am?"

Peter replied, "Thou art the Christ, the Son of the living God."

Jesus said to him, "Blessed art thou, Simon Bar-Jonah: for flesh and blood hath not revealed it unto thee, but my Father which is in heaven. I say to thee, that thou art Peter, and upon this rock I will build my church; and the gates of hell shall not prevail against it. I will give unto thee the keys of the kingdom."

Turning to the others, Jesus said, "Tell no man that I am the Christ."

*Jesus asks his disciples who the people say that he, the Son of Man,
is; he is pleased by Peter's confession that he is the Christ.*

Jesus goes up into a mountain with three of his disciples, Peter, James, and John, and is transfigured before them.

This is my beloved Son, in whom I am well pleased

JESUS HAD invited three of the disciples, Peter, James, and John, to go with him up one of the slopes of Mount Hermon, not far from Caesarea Philippi. After a few hours' climb, they stood looking out upon the great sweep of land below them. They could see many countries, and far to the south lay the Sea of Galilee.

As they stood there, suddenly Jesus' figure became swathed in a dazzling light. His face shone as the sun, and his garments became white as the light. And while the disciples gazed at Jesus' shining figure, Moses and Elijah appeared within the blaze of light, talking with Jesus.

Only Peter dared to speak. "Lord," he said to Jesus, "it is good for us to be here. And if thou wilt, I will make here three tabernacles: one for thee, and one for Moses, and one for Elijah."

Jesus did not reply, but as the three men watched, a bright cloud overshadowed them, and a voice spoke from the cloud. "This is my beloved Son, in whom I am well pleased; hear ye him."

Then the disciples were afraid and fell to their knees. They had never before seen Jesus revealed in heavenly form.

Jesus saw their fear, and coming near, touched them. "Arise," he said, "and be not afraid."

The quiet, familiar voice gave them courage. They had nothing to fear from the Master, who had been their companion and friend for many months.

Slowly, they got to their feet. And when they raised their eyes, the figures of Moses and Elijah had disappeared and the light was gone. They saw no one but Jesus.

*O faithless and perverse generation,
how long shall I bear with you?*

THE DAY after Jesus' transfiguration on the slopes of Mount Hermon, he and the three disciples came down from the mountain by way of a path that led into a poor, untidy village. Many of the villagers had taken refuge from the noonday heat under the *succôths*, the reed booths erected on the roofs of their low mud houses. But when Jesus entered the village, most of the people came out to greet him, for word of the new prophet from Nazareth and his healing power had spread throughout Palestine.

Jesus was about to speak to the villagers, when a man dashed out from among them, crying, "Master, I beseech thee to look upon my son; for he is mine only child: and behold, a spirit taketh him, and he suddenly crieth out; and it teareth him and he foameth, and it hardly departeth from him, bruising him sorely. And I besought thy disciples to cast it out; and they could not."

The disciples had lacked the faith necessary to help this man, even after many months of companionship with Jesus. "O faithless and perverse generation," he said to them, "how long shall I be with you, and bear with you?"

Then, turning to the father, he said, "Bring thy son hither."

The father rushed back to his house to fetch his son, and even as he led him toward Jesus, the boy was seized with violent illness.

Looking down at the sick boy, Jesus spoke a few words. Immediately he became quiet, and rose to his feet, strong and well. And all the villagers were amazed at the mighty power of God.

94

Coming down from the mountain, Jesus heals a boy from whom his disciples had failed to cast out a devil.

95

Go, and sin no more

JESUS WAS visiting in Jerusalem and had gone to the temple as was his custom. As he walked along one of the beautiful porticos that surrounded the temple courts, a group of his enemies brought to him a woman taken in adultery.

"Now we have this man where we may accuse him," they murmured among themselves. "If he speaks kindly to her, he will be breaking the Mosaic Law, which says an adulterous woman must be stoned. If he condemns her, he will be denying his own teaching."

They asked Jesus, "What sayest thou of her?" Smugly they waited, as the woman dropped to the floor.

Jesus stooped down and with his finger outlined some words on the marble floor, as though he had not heard the question. Annoyed, the woman's accusers repeated their charge. "This woman hath been taken in adultery. Now Moses commanded us in the Law that such should be stoned: but what sayest thou?"

Looking straight at the unmerciful men, Jesus said, "He that is without sin among you, let him first cast a stone at her."

The men had no answer. Convicted by their own conscience, they went out one by one, leaving Jesus and the woman alone in the portico.

Jesus stooped to write again. When he looked up and saw no one but the woman, he asked, "Where are those thine accusers? Hath no man condemned thee?"

For the first time, the woman spoke. "No man, Lord," she said.

Then Jesus said unto her, "Neither do I condemn thee: go, and sin no more."

Jesus, being asked to judge a woman taken in adultery, bids those who are without sin to cast the first stone at her.

Jesus, having cleansed ten lepers, is grieved that only one returns to give thanks, and he a stranger.

Were not the ten cleansed?
But where are the nine?

THE TIME had come when Jesus' ministry in Galilee must end, for now he must go into Judea. No spiritual leader of the Jews could call his work complete until he had carried his message to Jerusalem, the political and religious capital of the Jewish world.

On a day in October, Jesus and his disciples set out on the highway that ran south from Galilee to Jerusalem. As they crossed the border into Samaria, on the outskirts of a small village, a group of ten lepers met them. One was a Samaritan; the others were Jews. On seeing Jesus, they lifted up their voices and cried, "Jesus, Master, have mercy on us."

Jesus had compassion for them, but to test their faith he said, "Go and show yourselves unto the priests."

The men started on their way, the Jews to Jerusalem and the Samaritan to Mount Gerizim, the Samaritan center of worship. And as they went, their leprosy was cured.

Overjoyed, nine of the men threw away their canes and crutches and rushed home to show themselves to their families. Only one, the Samaritan, returned to give thanks to Jesus and to glorify God.

As the grateful Samaritan knelt at Jesus' feet, Jesus looked beyond him to the other men, hurrying down the road to the village.

"Were not the ten cleansed?" he asked. "But where are the nine? Were there none found that returned to give glory to God, save this stranger?"

Then, looking down at the man who clasped his hand in gratitude, Jesus said, "Arise and go thy way. Thy faith hath made thee whole."

Mary hath chosen the good part

TWO SISTERS, Mary and Martha, lived with their brother Lazarus in the little village of Bethany. Bethany was located on a slope of the Mount of Olives, about an hour's walk from Jerusalem.

The two sisters and their brother had become followers of Jesus, and he often stayed at their home during his visits to Jerusalem. After a day of teaching in the temple, the hospitable home of his three friends was a quiet refuge.

One day Jesus arrived in Bethany unexpectedly. Martha, the older sister, began to hurry about, preparing his chamber and getting milk and bread and dates on the table for his meal. Mary, the quieter sister, went with Jesus out into the garden, where they began to talk earnestly together.

Weighed down with household duties, Martha grew irritated. Self-pity, and perhaps a little jealousy, finally drove her out to the garden to complain to Jesus about her sister:

"Lord, dost thou not care that my sister did leave me to serve alone? Bid her therefore that she help me."

Lazarus, the brother, stood by. He thought, "What will Jesus say to my two sisters, so unlike each other in mind and spirit?"

Gently, Jesus spoke to the older sister, who was giving all her attention to her household duties. Somebody must prepare meals and tidy the house. "But Martha," Jesus said to her, "thou art anxious and troubled about many things: but one thing is needful; and Mary hath chosen the good part, which shall not be taken away from her."

100

He rests at Bethany in the house of his friends, Martha, Mary, and
Lazarus.

©Providence Lithograph Company

Jesus blesses little children, and chides those disciples who would keep them from him.

Suffer the little children to come unto me

IT WAS THE custom in Judea for parents to bring their children to the synagogue, to receive the rabbi's blessing. So the followers of Jesus, too, brought their children to him for his blessing.

Jesus and his disciples had come on a preaching and teaching mission to Perea, a small country east of Judea. As they entered one of the villages of Perea, a group of mothers, carrying or leading their small children, stopped Jesus at the gate.

It had been a long and busy day, and Jesus was tired. The disciples were tired, too, and hungry. In spite of their months with Jesus, they often forgot the nature of his mission and became impatient with the people who made selfish demands upon the Master. Now they rebuked the mothers who gathered about Jesus and tried to send them away.

When Jesus saw the disciples' lack of compassion and heard their sharp words to the mothers, he was moved with indignation. "Suffer the little children to come unto me," he said. "Forbid them not, for of such is the Kingdom of Heaven."

The Kingdom of Heaven for children? It was difficult for the disciples to understand that.

"Verily I say unto you," Jesus continued. "Whosoever shall not receive the Kingdom of God as a little child, he shall in no wise enter therein."

The disciples watched, silent and ashamed, as more mothers came out through the village gate with their children.

Then Jesus took the children in his arms, and put his hands upon them, and blessed them.

If thou believedst, thou wouldst see the glory of God

LAZARUS, THE brother of Mary and Martha, was very sick. Although Jesus was in Perea, the sisters sent word to him to come to Bethany. "He whom thou lovest is sick," they said.

When Jesus received their message, he said, "This sickness is not unto death, but for the glory of God, that the Son of God might be glorified thereby."

And he waited two days before he left for Bethany. And when he arrived there, Lazarus had died.

With the two sisters and the friends who had come to the home to comfort them, Jesus went to the tomb of the dead man. A stone lay against the entrance to the tomb, and Jesus said to Martha, "Take ye away the stone."

"Lord, he hath been dead four days," Martha said.

But Jesus said to her, "Said I not unto thee, that, if thou believedst, thou shouldst see the glory of God?"

So they took away the stone, and Jesus began to pray.

"Father, I thank thee that thou hast heard me: because of the multitude which standeth around, I said it, that they may believe that thou didst send me."

When he had finished his prayer, Jesus spoke with a loud voice, "Lazarus, come forth."

Lazarus came forth from the tomb, his burial clothes about him.

"Loose him, and let him go," Jesus said.

Many of those who had seen the miracle followed Jesus. Others reported to the Pharisees what had happened.

Jesus raises Lazarus from the dead.

Jesus summons Zacchaeus the publican to entertain him at his house.

This day is salvation come to this house

JESUS WAS still in Perea at the time of the Passover, and he joined the pilgrims going to Jerusalem to celebrate the holy days.

The highway leading west, toward Judea, was crowded with people. Sometimes, as they walked or rode their little donkeys, they sang. And when they crossed the Jordan River and could look back on the highlands of their own country, they chanted the ancient psalm of their fathers: *I will lift up mine eyes unto the hills.*

At the city of Jericho, two highways met, and when Jesus and his companions reached the city, it was thronged with pilgrims. Word had come to Jericho that the prophet from Nazareth would pass that way. One man, Zacchaeus, who was short of stature, climbed a sycamore tree to see Jesus better when he passed. Zacchaeus was a wealthy publican, one of the tax collectors distrusted by the people.

When Jesus reached the place where Zacchaeus was, he looked up and said to him, "Zacchaeus, make haste and come down; for today I must abide at thy house."

When the enemies of Jesus saw him going home with a publican, they murmured, "He is gone in to be guest with a sinner."

At Zacchaeus' abundant table, Jesus told the publican of the Kingdom of Heaven and what was required to enter it.

Zacchaeus said, "Behold, Lord, the half of my goods I give to the poor; and if I have taken anything from any man by false accusation, I restore it to him fourfold."

Then Jesus said, "This day is salvation come to this house. The Son of Man is come to seek and to save that which is lost."

107

Go thy way; thy faith hath made thee whole

JERICHO WAS known as the city of palm trees. Groves of balsam, spice, and fruit-bearing trees added to its beauty. Herod the Great had chosen Jericho as a summer residence and had improved the city with graceful aqueducts, public baths, and a handsome theater.

But there was suffering and sorrow amid the beauty of Jericho. Blindness was common there, as throughout Palestine. The blind from the families of the poor begged for food along the roads.

As Jesus went on his way from the home of Zacchaeus, through the city gate leading to the Jerusalem highway, he heard a voice crying, "Jesus, thou son of David, have mercy on me!"

A blind beggar sitting near the gate to beg from the Passover crowds had heard that the new prophet was passing by and was calling to him for help.

"Hold thy peace!" The hurrying pilgrims rebuked the beggar, but he only cried out the louder.

Jesus stood still. "Call ye him," he said to the people standing near. Quickly the mood of his companions changed. The prophet wished to speak to this beggar. Suddenly the unfortunate man became worthy of their attention, too.

"Be of good cheer: rise, he calleth thee," they told him.

The beggar, casting away his garment, sprang up and came to Jesus.

"What wilt thou that I should do unto thee?" Jesus asked him.

"Rabboni, that I may receive my sight."

"Go thy way; thy faith hath made thee whole," Jesus said. And at once the blind man received his sight, and followed Jesus in the Way.

Leaving Jericho, Jesus restores sight to blind Bartimaeus who sat by the wayside begging.

© Providence Lithograph Company

Jesus, riding on the foal of an ass, enters Jerusalem, as the people shout, "Hosanna to the son of David."

110

Blessed is he that cometh in the name of the Lord

AFTER JESUS reached Jerusalem, he went on a few miles to the home of Mary and Martha and Lazarus in the town of Bethany.

The following morning he started out early for the walk into the city. He was soon joined by pilgrims going to the temple at Jerusalem.

As they approached the village of Bethphage, Jesus said to two of the disciples, "Go into the village over against you, and straightway ye shall find an ass tied, and a colt with her: loose them, and bring them unto me. And if any man say aught unto you, ye shall say, 'The Lord hath need of them'; and straightaway he will send them."

The disciples did as Jesus bade, and brought the ass and its colt back. They made a seat of their garments and put it on the ass that Jesus might ride into Jerusalem. Thus was fulfilled the prophecy:

Tell ye the daughter of Zion: Behold, thy King cometh unto thee, meek, and riding upon an ass, and upon a colt the foal of an ass.

As the small procession continued toward the city, more people joined it, all in happy festival mood. Suddenly, as they approached the Golden Gate, they burst into song.

Lift up your heads, O ye gates, and be ye lifted up, ye everlasting doors, and the King of Glory shall come in.

By this time a very great multitude had come together with Jesus. Some spread their garments in the road before him; others cut down branches from the trees and lay them in the way. And all the multitudes cried, "Hosanna to the son of David: Blessed is he that cometh in the name of the Lord: Hosanna in the highest."

*By what authority
doest thou these things?*

EVERY DAY during the Passover, Jesus taught in the temple. The chief priests and the scribes and other principal men sought how they might destroy him, for the people hung on his words.

Today, in one of the great outer courts, the crowds were listening to Jesus preaching the Gospel. In strong words he denounced the hypocrisy of many of the temple worshipers.

"The Kingdom of God shall be taken from you, and given to a nation bringing forth the fruits thereof," he warned.

The high priests and scribes and elders looked on, anger in their hearts. They did not dare attack Jesus openly, for he was too popular with the people. They would silence him with trickery.

"By what authority doest thou these things?" they asked him one day. If he answered, "On the authority of God," they would accuse him of blasphemy, which was punishable by death from stoning.

"I also will ask you a question," Jesus replied. "And tell me: the baptism of John, was it from heaven or from men?"

The high priests reasoned among themselves: "If we shall say 'From heaven,' he will say, 'Then why did ye not believe him?' But if we shall say, 'From men,' all the people will stone us, for they were persuaded that John was a prophet."

And they answered that they knew not from which it was.

Then Jesus said unto them, "Neither tell I you by what authority I do these things."

Humiliated and angry, the scribes and priests left the court, and Jesus began again to teach the people.

Jesus thereafter teaches daily in the temple, and the priests demand of him by what authority he does those things.

Lord, not my feet only, but also my hands and my head

KNOWING THAT he was soon to die, Jesus had asked his disciples to hire a large upper room in Jerusalem, where they might eat together the Passover Feast—the *Seder* meal. The disciples had had the paschal lamb cooked whole, as required by law, with no bones broken, and had taken part of it to the temple altars. The remainder they had brought back to the upper room for the feast. Bitter herbs dipped in sweet sauce, unleavened bread, and four cups of red wine completed the meal, which Jesus and his twelve friends ate, reclining about the low table. The small clay lamps, in the candelabra overhead, shone softly down. It was a happy gathering for most of the disciples, but the devil had put it into the heart of Judas Iscariot to betray Jesus.

No one had offered, as was customary before a feast, to perform the ritual of foot-washing. So, after the meal, Jesus took a towel, poured water into a basin, and began to wash the disciples' feet himself.

The disciples looked on in shamed silence, but when Jesus came to Peter, he cried out, "Lord, dost thou wash my feet?"

Jesus answered, "What I do thou knowest not now; but thou shalt understand hereafter."

Then Peter said, "Thou shalt never wash my feet."

"If I wash thee not," Jesus replied, "thou hast no part of me."

Humbly, Peter cried, "Lord, not my feet only, but also my hands and my head."

Then Jesus said to him, "He that is bathed needeth not save to wash his feet, but is clean every whit: and ye are clean, but not all."

©Providence Lithograph Company

Jesus, with the Twelve, partakes of the Passover Feast in an upper chamber. He teaches humility by washing the disciples' feet.

115

© Providence Lithograph Company

Thereafter Jesus breaks bread, and gives the disciples the cup, commanding them to do this in remembrance of him.

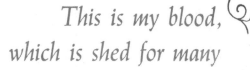

WHEN JESUS had finished washing the disciples' feet, he returned to the table. He was troubled in spirit, and looking about him at the twelve men, he said, "Verily, I say unto you that one of you shall betray me."

Shocked at Jesus' words, the disciples looked at one another, doubting of whom he spoke. Perhaps John, the beloved disciple, who was sitting next to Jesus, would know to whom the Master referred.

Beckoning John, Peter whispered to him, "Tell us who it is of whom he speaketh."

"Lord, who is it?" John asked Jesus, and Jesus replied, "He it is for whom I shall dip the sop and give it to him."

The sop was made up of bits of lamb, bread, and herbs. It was customary to hand it to a guest as a gesture of good will. Now Jesus prepared the sop and handed it to Judas, saying, "That thou doest, do quickly."

None of the other disciples understood why Jesus spoke these words to Judas. Some thought he was asking Judas, who held their money, to buy something for the Passover.

Judas took the sop from Jesus' hand and dashed out into the night.

Puzzled and silent, the disciples continued the meal. As they ate, Jesus took bread, and when he had blessed it, he broke it, and gave it to the disciples, saying, "Take ye: this is my body."

Then Jesus took a cup of wine, and when he had given thanks, he gave it to them; and they all drank of it. And he said to them, "This is my blood of the New Testament, which is shed for many."

© 1957 Providence Lithograph Company

Jesus then proceeds to Gethsemane with his disciples, where, going apart from them, he prays in agony of spirit.

Watch and pray, that ye enter not into temptation

JESUS WAS sorrowful and troubled as he and the disciples left the upper room and went out into the city. "Let us go up into the Mount of Olives," he said to his friends. A deep grove of olive trees, known as Gethsemane, was his retreat on the mountain. Here he often came to be alone.

When they reached the grove, Jesus said to the disciples, "Sit ye here, while I go yonder and pray." Taking Peter and James and John with him, he went deeper into the grove.

"My soul is exceedingly sorrowful, even unto death," he said to the three companions. "Abide ye here, and watch with me." And walking a short distance from them, he fell on his knees and prayed:

"O my Father, if it be possible, let this cup pass away from me: nevertheless, not as I will, but as thou wilt."

When he came back to the three disciples, he found them sleeping. It had been a long and tiring day, but Jesus did not expect this of Peter. "What," he said to him, "could ye not watch with me one hour? Watch and pray, that ye enter not into temptation: the spirit indeed is willing, but the flesh is weak."

He left them a second time, and prayed, saying, "O my Father, if this cannot pass away, except I drink it, thy will be done." Returning to the disciples, he found them asleep.

A third time Jesus left the disciples, and again they slept. Finally, Jesus said to them, "Sleep on now, and take your rest: the Son of Man is betrayed unto the hands of sinners. Arise, let us go."

AS JESUS and his friends were about to leave Gethsemane, they heard voices and the clanking of arms. Soon the glare of torches revealed a band of soldiers, accompanied by servants of the high priests and Pharisees.

Knowing why they had come, Jesus stepped forward. "Whom seek ye?" he asked.

"Jesus of Nazareth," the captain answered.

"I am he," Jesus said, and at his words, the soldiers and servants stepped back quickly. Then Judas, who was with them, and who had arranged to identify Jesus with a kiss, stepped to Jesus' side.

"Hail, Rabbi," he said to Jesus, and kissed him.

Looking sadly upon the traitor, Jesus said, "Friend, do that for which thou art come."

Judas did not answer, and the soldiers came and seized Jesus to take him away. But Simon Peter drew a sword and cut off the right ear of one of the servants. It was a brave gesture, but it would serve no purpose, and Jesus said to Peter: "Put up again thy sword: for all they that take the sword shall perish with the sword. Thinkest thou that I cannot beseech my Father, and he shall send me more than twelve legions of angels? How then should the Scriptures be fulfilled?"

Turning to the soldiers he said, "Are ye come out as against a robber with swords and staves to seize me? I sat daily in the temple teaching, and ye took me not. But all this is come to pass, that the Scriptures of the prophets might be fulfilled."

Then all the disciples left him, and fled.

Judas, having received a band of men and officers from the priests, follows them to Gethsemane, and there betrays Jesus with a kiss.

121

THE STREETS of Jerusalem were dark as Jesus was led down into the city. The clanging of the soldiers' sandals brought curious folks peering from their chambers. "Someone is in trouble with the Roman guard," they muttered, and went back to their beds.

The little procession continued to the palace of Caiaphas, the High Priest. Nobody noticed a furtive figure, following from afar off in the shadows.

At the palace, the chief priests sought false witness against Jesus, that they might put him to death, but they could find no cause for his death, though many false witnesses spoke against him. Finally two men testified, "This man said, 'I am able to destroy the temple of God, and to build it in three days.'"

The High Priest looked at Jesus in pretended horror. "Answerest thou nothing? What is it which these witness against thee?"

But Jesus would not reply. Then the High Priest said to him, "I adjure thee by the living God, that thou tell us whether thou be the Christ, the Son of God."

Jesus answered, "Thou hast said: nevertheless I say unto you, henceforth ye shall see the Son of Man sitting at the right hand of power, and coming on the clouds of heaven."

It had all been cunningly planned. The High Priest tore his robe the length of his palm, as the Law required him to do when blasphemy was uttered, and cried out to those sitting in judgment, "He hath spoken blasphemy: what further need have we of witnesses? What think ye?"

Quickly the judges answered. "He is worthy of death."

Jesus, brought before the High Priest Caiaphas and the Council, is accused of blasphemy and condemned.

123

WHEN THE verdict against Jesus was announced, a silent figure wept. It was Peter, who had fled Gethsemane, but who had crept back to witness the scene he had not had the courage to share.

As he sat in the court, trembling at the sight of his Lord being led away to his death, a young maid looked at him curiously.

"Thou also wast with Jesus the Galilean," she said.

Terrified, Peter denied it. "I know not what thou sayest," he protested, and fled to the porch.

There a second maid saw him, and reported to her master, "This man also was with Jesus the Nazarene."

Again Peter denied it, and swore to his statement with an oath.

Why had he come here? What torment had driven him to walk into such danger? While he chided himself, a third accuser approached him. "Of a truth thou also art one of them; for thy Galilean speech betrayeth thee."

In a panic of fear, Peter began to curse and to swear, "I know not the man."

Just at that moment, Jesus passed by with the guards. Turning, he looked straight at Peter, the man he had once called a "rock." And Peter remembered that Jesus had said, "Before the cock crow this day, thou shalt deny me thrice."

Roughly, the guards pushed Jesus along through the court of Caiaphas' beautiful palace. With a pleading look at his Lord, Peter rushed out. As he went into the night, he heard the cock crow to welcome the new day.

Peter, having denied his Master three times before cock crow, repents as Jesus turns and looks upon him.

What accusation bring ye against this man?

THE GUARDS who led Jesus from the palace of Caiaphas treated him cruelly. They struck him, spat upon him, and mocked him. "Prophesy unto us, thou Christ," they jeered.

When morning came, the Sanhedrin was called together. Hungry, cold, and sore from blows, Jesus was brought to the temple area where the Sanhedrin met. Early worshipers were already entering the temple to wait for the sunrise and for the Passover ritual to begin.

"What need we of any further witness?" the members of the Sanhedrin said. "For we ourselves have heard it from his own mouth."

But they could not condemn a man to death without the consent of the Roman governor. So they brought Jesus to the palace of Pilate, the Roman governor of Judea. Pilate was in Jerusalem during the Passover celebration out of courtesy to his Jewish subjects.

The chief priests and scribes could not enter the heathen palace, lest they be defiled and unfit to celebrate the Passover. They stood outside, and Pilate came out to them.

"What accusation bring ye against this man?" Pilate asked.

"If he were not a malefactor, we would not have delivered him up unto thee," the scribes answered.

Then they began their accusations, saying, "We found him perverting our nation, and forbidding to give tribute to Caesar, and saying that he himself is Christ, a king."

Thus they included in their charges crimes against the Roman government, thinking to turn Pilate against their victim.

Jesus, his wrists shackled to a guard, stood by and listened in silence.

Early in the morning Jesus is brought to Pilate, the governor, and accused before him.

PILATE LOOKED at Jesus and back to the shouting accusers. He knew that this hasty proceeding would never have the approval of Rome. He therefore entered his palace again and asked that Jesus be brought before him. He would question him in private.

The room in which Pilate carried on his government affairs was handsomely furnished. Rich tapestries hung from the walls. Busts of the Caesars, on imposing pedestals, spoke of the wealth and power of Rome. Magnificent columns rose from the beautiful marble floor.

Pilate sat on his luxurious couch and looked at the man who stood before him, his wrists still in shackles.

"Art thou the King of the Jews?" Pilate asked.

Jesus answered with a question. "Art thou asking me this for thyself, or did someone say this concerning me?"

"Thine own nation and the chief priests delivered thee unto me," Pilate answered. "What hast thou done?"

"My kingdom is not of this world," Jesus said. "If my kingdom were of this world, then would my servants fight: but now is my kingdom not from hence."

"Art thou a king then?" Pilate asked again.

And Jesus answered, "To this end was I born, and to this end am I come into the world, that I should bear witness unto the truth. Everyone that is of the truth heareth my voice."

Pilate believed Jesus was innocent, but outside the palace, the leaders of this man's own people made grave charges against him.

Half to himself, the puzzled governor asked, "What is truth?"

Pilate privately examines Jesus regarding his claims to kingship.

© 1957 Providence Lithograph Company

Pilate, learning that Jesus belongs to another jurisdiction, sends him to Herod.

SATISFIED OF THE innocence of Jesus, Pilate had him led back to the people waiting outside the palace.

"I find no fault in this man," Pilate said. Then the crowd grew more urgent. Some of the leaders shouted, "He stirreth up the people, teaching throughout all Judea, and beginning from Galilee even unto this place."

"Is this man a Galilean?" Pilate asked quickly.

If he were a Galilean, he was not of Pilate's jurisdiction.

"Yea, of Nazareth," was the reply.

"Then take him to Herod," Pilate ordered. "Herod Antipas is governor of Galilee. Let him deal with this man."

Herod was also in the city for the Passover, and once more Jesus was hurried away, this time to Herod's palace in Jerusalem.

When Herod saw Jesus he was glad, for he had wished for a long time to see him. "We will have him perform some miracles for us," he mockingly said to the ladies of his court.

The arrogant Herod asked Jesus many questions, but Jesus, knowing how useless speech would be, answered him nothing. And while Jesus remained silent, the chief priests and scribes standing by continued to accuse him.

Herod became angered at Jesus' silence. The vain governor was being humiliated before his court. He would mock this "king" by ordering his soldiers to put a royal robe on him.

The soldiers did so, and Herod laughed scornfully. "Take him back to Pilate," he ordered.

PILATE'S SCHEME for turning Jesus over to Herod had not worked, and now the prisoner was back at Pilate's palace.

Calling the chief priests and the rulers together, he said to them: "Ye brought unto me this man, as one that perverteth the people, and behold, I, having examined him before you, found no fault in this man touching those things whereof ye accuse him. No, nor yet Herod, for he sent him back unto us; and behold, nothing worthy of death hath been done by him. I will therefore chastise him, and release him."

It was the custom for the governor of a Jewish province to release a condemned criminal during the Passover.

"Whom will I release unto you?" Pilate asked the mob. "Barabbas or Jesus?" Barabbas had been condemned to death for insurrection and murder. Surely, Pilate thought, the crowd would choose Jesus for release rather than the murderer.

But the crowd cried out together, "Barabbas! Away with this man and release unto us Barabbas!"

Again Pilate tried to change their minds, and again they cried, "Crucify him! Crucify him!"

So Pilate prepared to deliver Jesus to them, to deal with him as they would. But first he must keep his word and chastise Jesus himself.

Calling two menservants, he ordered them to tie Jesus to the whipping stone and strip his garments from his back. Then, in sight of a soldier of Rome and some passers-by, the men lashed Jesus with cruel blows, while the timid Pilate looked on.

Herod sends him back to Pilate, who delivers him to be scourged.

133

Jesus, arrayed in mock state, is brutally treated by the Roman soldiers.

ROME DID NOT usually send her best soldiers to the foreign service. She assigned the poorest of her standing armies to the province of Palestine. Even Roman governing officials were sometimes ordered to Palestine as a form of punishment.

So it was that after his savage beating in Pilate's outer court, Jesus was released to the care of a group of ignorant soldiers from one of Rome's many foreign provinces. These men had none of the personal dignity or pride in the Empire that the native Roman soldier possessed.

When the soldiers in Pilate's service took Jesus from the whipping stone to the barrack room, they called their whole company together. They would amuse themselves at this man's expense.

The untidy barrack room reflected the characters of the men who were quartered in it. The air was foul, the furnishings scarred and dirty.

Gleefully the soldiers stripped Jesus of his torn garment. Somebody found a worn purple robe and they put this on his back. They plaited a crown of thorns and crushed it down over his bruised forehead and placed a reed in his hand.

Some of these soldiers had seen the "carnival king" in Mesopotamia, the mock king who was elected during a festival to be whipped and hanged for public entertainment. This man would be their carnival king. They knelt before him and laughed loudly at their humor. One of them scrawled "Ave Rex" on the wall over his head. "Hail, King of the Jews!" they cried. Then they spat upon him and took the reed from his hand and struck him on the head.

Pilate, declaring himself guiltless of the blood of Jesus, nevertheless yields him to be crucified.

Crucify him! Crucify him!

MESSENGERS from Pilate interrupted the amusement of the soldiers. The governor had sent for Jesus.

By this time, a noisy rabble had gathered about the palace. Pilate was afraid. If these Jewish leaders should complain to Rome about his bad government, he would be in trouble. He must keep the high priests and scribes and members of the Sanhedrin appeased.

Once again, the governor ordered Jesus brought out before the screaming mob, hoping that the sight of his suffering might soften their hearts.

Jesus stood before them, wearing the purple robe and the crown of thorns. Pilate addressed the crowd: "Behold, I bring him forth to you, that ye may know that I find no fault in him."

But the chief priests and officers cried out the louder, "Crucify him!"

"What evil hath he done?" Pilate cried above the noise of the mob.

"Let him be crucified!" they shouted back.

Pilate saw that he could do no more. But to make his position clear to the crowd, he resorted to one of their own customs. For a person to wash his hands in public meant that he took no responsibility for whatever was going on at the time. Pilate ordered a basin of water to be brought to him and he washed his hands before the mob.

"I am innocent of the blood of this man," he said.

And all the people standing before the palace shouted, "His blood be on us, and on our children."

Then Pilate released Barabbas for the Passover, and delivered Jesus to the mob to be crucified.

ROMAN SOLDIERS took Jesus through the long, narrow street that led from Pilate's palace to the temple area.

The Jewish law demanded that certain conditions be met at the time of an execution. The victim must be taken to the place of execution during the daylight hours. A herald must go ahead, calling out the crime for which he was being executed. A representative of the Sanhedrin must witness the death.

Some of these requirements were met, as Jesus made his painful way to the small hill where he would be crucified. But there were more witnesses than the law called for, because this prophet from Nazareth was more widely known than most men sentenced to die. Among the crowd following Jesus as he bore his own cross were many of his followers. A weeping woman brought him a drink.

As Jesus fell under the weight of the cross, a soldier called a man standing near, Simon from Cyrene, and ordered him to carry the cross.

More and more of the women of Jerusalem, most of them not disciples, joined the procession and wept in compassion for the suffering man. Seeing them, Jesus stopped and began to prophesy the destruction of Jerusalem.

"Daughters of Jerusalem, weep not for me, but weep for yourselves, and for your children. For, behold, the days are coming, in which they shall say, 'Blessed are the barren, and the wombs that never bare, and the breasts that never gave suck.' Then shall they begin to say to the mountains, 'Fall on us'; and to the hills, 'Cover us'. For if they do these things in the green tree, what shall be done in the dry?"

Jesus, sinking under the weight of his cross, bids the sorrowing women to weep not for him but for themselves.

139

Father, forgive them, for they know not what they do

DEATH BY crucifixion was a degrading form of punishment, because it held the victim up to public view, and his suffering was long drawn out. Crucifixion was reserved for slaves, thieves, and criminals who were not Roman citizens. It was not a Jewish form of punishment, but it was the choice of the enemies of Jesus.

Because executions must not be carried out within the city walls, Jesus was brought outside the Ephraim Gate to a small hill called Calvary, meaning "skull." Calvary Hill was situated along a busy road that led from the coastal town of Jaffa to Jerusalem.

To the crowd that had come out from the city there were now added curious travelers and passers-by. Other people, hurrying into Jerusalem for the Passover, did not stop to see what was going on.

At the foot of the hill, the hired executioners went to work. They stripped Jesus of his garment, tied him to the cross, and drove nails through his hands and feet. Then they raised the cross to an upright position. As Jesus hung from the cross in agony, two members of the Sanhedrin stood by, reading the parchment required by law for recording the crime of the victim.

Their job done, the executioners cast lots for the garments of Jesus. The victim's garments were considered part of their wages.

Two other crosses, each bearing the body of a thief, were raised on either side of the cross of Jesus.

Above the talk of the crowd, and the weeping of Jesus' followers, few heard his words: "Father, forgive them, for they know not what they do."

© 1957 Providence Lithograph Company

Coming to a place called Calvary, Jesus is there crucified and two others with him.

©1957 Providence Lithograph Company

Jesus charges John with the care of his mother.

Woman, behold thy son.
Behold thy mother

FOR THREE HOURS Jesus suffered on the cross. On one of the crosses beside him a crucified robber reviled him. On the other cross, a penitent man asked and received forgiveness for his sins. "Today shalt thou be with me in Paradise," Jesus said to him.

The soldiers mocked him and his enemies sneered. "He saved others; himself he cannot save," they cried. And that all passers-by might see the humiliation of this false prophet, they posted a crudely lettered inscription above his head: THIS IS THE KING OF THE JEWS.

Some of the crowd had left now. The excitement was over. But there were those who lingered at Calvary. John was there—the sturdy fisherman whom Jesus had called with his brother as they mended their nets by the shore of the Sea of Galilee. The mother of Jesus was there, and Mary Magdalene, and the other Mary.

In the last moments of life, Jesus looked down and saw his mother, with John standing near her.

"Woman, behold thy son," Jesus said to his mother. And to John, "Behold thy mother."

And from that hour, John took Mary into his own home.

"I thirst," Jesus murmured. A soldier filled a sponge with vinegar, and put it on hyssop, and raised it to Jesus' mouth to ease the pain.

When Jesus had received the vinegar, he said, "It is finished," and he bowed his head in death.

Soldiers came to break the legs of the three men to hasten their death. They saw Jesus was already dead, but one of them drew his sword and pierced Jesus' side, and blood and water came forth.

Into thy hands
I commend my spirit

IT WAS the sixth hour, the legal hour of sunset in Palestine. Down in the great temple in the city, the High Priest was opening the first Passover ceremony. Three sharp blasts were sounded on the trumpets. The High Priest ascended the marble steps to the altars of sacrifice, and the Levites chanted, "Praise ye the Lord."

On Calvary Hill, Jesus had died. The few watchers at the cross had heard him cry out in the dusk, "Father, into thy hands I commend my spirit."

Suddenly the city of Jerusalem became shrouded in a murky blackness, and the hills about the city quivered as though they had been shaken by an earthquake. The veil before the Holy Place in the temple was rent in two.

At the foot of the cross a Roman centurion stood guard. The last of the weeping friends of Jesus were leaving. They could do no more. The scribes and the priests had long since departed for the ceremonies at the temple. But the centurion must stay on to guard the bodies of the dead.

The Roman soldier had not been impressed by all that had taken place. He had merely been doing his duty. But he had heard the final, agonized cry of this dying man to his God. And at that very moment, the earth began to shake beneath his feet.

"Certainly, this was a righteous man," the centurion said, and he began to glorify God.

And all the people who had been at the cross returned home, smiting their breasts.

Jesus yields up the ghost, and the multitude return to their homes in fear of what they have seen.

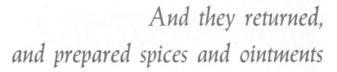

And they returned,
and prepared spices and ointments

THE JEWISH LAW forbade leaving a body upon a cross over-night. The body of Jesus must therefore be removed, but Pilate's consent was needed. Pilate had disapproved of the crucifixion of Jesus and would not want to be troubled further. Who had enough influence to approach the Roman governor again?

"What of Joseph of Arimathea?" somebody asked. Joseph was a member of the Sanhedrin, a righteous man, who was looking for the Kingdom of God, and Joseph had not consented to the death of Jesus.

Joseph was willing to go to Pilate to ask for the body of the man in whose innocence he believed. Furthermore, he would bury the body in a tomb in which no man had yet lain, even though the law forbade giving an honorable burial to one whom the Sanhedrin had condemned to death.

Pilate gave his consent, and Joseph had the body of Jesus taken from the cross, wrapped in two pieces of fine linen, and buried in a new tomb, hewn out of a rock in a quiet garden not far from Joseph's home.

Certain women who had loved and ministered to Jesus were not content with this burial. The body of their Lord must be properly anointed. So they followed Joseph's men to learn where Jesus was to be buried. Then they hurried home to prepare the necessary spices and ointments before the Sabbath Day.

Before sundown they returned to anoint with gentle hands the body of their Lord. As they did so, a stranger entered the tomb. He, too, brought ointments and costly myrrh and aloes. The timid Nicodemus had come to anoint the body of Jesus.

146

Joseph of Arimathea asks for the body of Jesus, and lays it in his own new tomb.

147

On the first day of the week come certain women to the sepulcher. They see a vision of angels who declare that Jesus is risen from the dead.

148

He is not here;
but is risen

ALL WAS QUIET in Jerusalem on the Sabbath. But at sundown Mary, the mother of Jesus, and Mary Magdalene, and Joanna made plans to go to the tomb. As it began to dawn toward the first day of the week, they hurried to Joseph's garden.

A few farmers, driving their small carts loaded with produce for the city markets, looked at the women curiously. Early risers heading for Job's Well, waterpots poised gracefully on their heads, nodded at the hurrying women. Where could they be going with neither baskets nor waterpots so early in the morning?

"How shall we roll the heavy stone away from the door?" Mary Magdalene asked her companions. They did not know.

Birds were singing and the sun's warmth had begun to dry the grass as the women approached the tomb. But what was this? The stone had already been rolled away! Quickly they entered the tomb. It was empty.

As the women stood speechless with fear, two angels in shining garments appeared. The women fell to their knees. "Why seek ye the living among the dead?" one angel said. "He is not here; but is risen. Remember how he spake unto you when he was yet in Galilee?"

Yes, they remembered. Jesus had said, "The Son of Man must be delivered into the hands of sinful men, and be crucified, and the third day rise again."

As quickly as they had come, the women hastened back along the road to the city. This time their hearts were light. They must find the eleven disciples and tell them the wonderful news: the tomb was empty. Their Lord had risen, even as he had said.

Peter and John hasten to the sepulcher; they see and believe.

ARY MAGDALENE, feeling worried and fear-ful, hurried to the lodgings of Peter and John in Jerusalem. The angel had said their Lord had risen, but where was his body?

She found Peter and John sitting sadly at a table, their untouched meal before them.

"Peter! John!" Mary cried. "They have taken away the Lord out of the sepulcher, and we know not where they have laid him."

The two disciples rushed from the house and out of the city. John, the younger, outran Peter and arrived at the tomb first. Stooping, he looked into the tomb. He saw the linen cloths in which the body had been wrapped; yet he did not enter the place of burial.

John was soon followed by Peter who entered the tomb at once. Peter, too, saw the linen cloths lying where the body had been, but the napkin that had been upon the head had been placed at one side.

"John! He is not here!" Peter's tone was hushed. Slowly John entered the tomb and looked upon the place where the body of their Lord had lain. And he saw, and believed.

Peter and John, in their fear, had forgotten the words of Scripture which said that Jesus must be crucified and must rise again from the dead. Silent with wonder, the two disciples left the garden and walked slowly down the road toward Jerusalem.

They had thought Mary Magdalene and the women who had been with her early at the tomb had seen visions and had told them idle tales, and they had not believed. Now, having seen the empty tomb, they wondered within themselves at that which had come to pass.

ARY MAGDALENE did not return to the city with Peter and John, but remained alone at the sepulcher, troubled and afraid. Their Lord had risen, but where had he gone?

As she wept, she looked into the tomb, and drew back in fright. Two angels sat within, one at the head and one at the foot of the place where the Lord's body had lain.

"Woman, why weepest thou?" the angels asked.

"Because they have taken away my Lord, and I know not where they have laid him."

The angels disappeared and Mary came out into the garden. A stranger had approached the tomb, but she did not hide her tears.

"Woman, why weepest thou? Whom seekest thou?"

This must be the gardener. "Sir, if thou hast borne him hence, tell me where thou hast laid him, and I will take him away."

"Mary."

Her heart leaped. It was the voice of the Master, and turning, she recognized the Lord.

"Rabboni!" Arms outstretched, she ran to Jesus.

"Mary, touch me not, for I am not yet ascended to my Father: but go unto my brethren, and say to them, I ascend unto my Father and your Father, and to my God and your God."

Once more, Mary hastened back to find the disciples. Why had she not believed that the Master would show himself to his loved ones? He had promised them that he would come again.

"Peter! John!" she called at their door. "I have seen the Lord!"

Jesus reveals himself to Mary Magdalene.

153

He draws nigh to two disciples journeying to Emmaus, and proves to them from the Scriptures that Jesus is truly Christ.

O foolish men, and slow of heart to believe

CLEOPAS, who was one of the seventy men whom Jesus had appointed as teachers, had business in Emmaus, the village of another of the seventy. The two men had left Jerusalem early.

They had little heart for business. The tragedy of the Master's death was still uppermost in their minds, and as they walked, they discussed all that had happened. Had they failed their Lord? Could they have influenced the Sanhedrin? Had Mary really seen the Master?

A short distance out of the city, a stranger overtook them—a curious stranger, it would seem, for he asked an abrupt question:

"What conversations are these that ye have as ye walk?"

Surprised, Cleopas answered, "Dost thou sojourn in Jerusalem and not know the things which are come to pass there in these days?"

"What things?"

"Concerning Jesus of Nazareth, a prophet mighty in deed and word before God. It is now the third day since he was crucified."

"Yes," said Cleopas' companion, "and certain women went to the tomb and found it empty, and saw visions of angels, which said Jesus was alive. Peter and John went to the tomb and found it even as the women said, but they saw not Jesus."

The three men were quiet for a moment. Then Cleopas said sadly, "We hoped that it was he which should redeem Israel."

Now the stranger began to speak, and the disciples were startled at his words. "O foolish men, and slow of heart to believe all that the prophets have spoken." And he continued to interpret all that the Scriptures said of the Son of God.

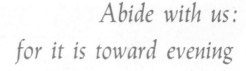

Abide with us: for it is toward evening

THE TWO MEN scarcely realized that they had reached Emmaus, so interested were they in this stranger's words. But when he was about to leave them, Cleopas said, "Abide with us: for it is toward evening, and the day is now far spent."

"Yes, come to my home and we shall sit at meat together," his friend urged. There were many more questions to ask this learned man.

So the three men went up on the cool roof of the Emmaus home to eat their evening meal. And then a strange thing happened. The guest, and not the host, took the loaf of bread from the table, broke it, and returned thanks.

Suddenly both men recognized their guest. It was the Master! But before they could speak, he had disappeared from their sight.

The meal and the late hour forgotten, Cleopas and his friend hurried back to Jerusalem to find the disciples. And they found them tense with excitement too. "The Lord is risen indeed, and hath appeared to Simon Peter," the disciples announced.

"Yes," Peter explained, "I saw him last night as I went about the streets." He could say no more, but his friends understood the bitter remorse of Peter, who had denied his Lord in the hour of trial.

"Tell my disciples, and Peter." The Master had singled him out for a special word when he spoke to Mary at the sepulcher. But how he longed to see Jesus himself and beg his forgiveness. And at last, as he crouched in the doorway of Caiaphas' home, Jesus had touched his shoulder and had spoken the words that Peter had heard him speak to so many others. "Thy sins are forgiven, Peter. Go, and sin no more."

Jesus appears to Simon Peter.

157

Again he appears to his disciples, and chides Thomas for his unbelief.

A WEEK HAD passed since Peter, John, and the women had found Jesus' tomb empty. During those days Jesus had appeared to several of his followers. They could not speak openly of these things, for their enemies were everywhere.

It was the evening of the first day after the Sabbath. Some of the disciples were praying together in the home of one, and as they prayed, Jesus came and stood in their midst.

"Peace be unto you," he said. And when he had said this, he showed them his hands and his side.

Thomas, one of the eleven disciples, was not with them, and when the others told him of this, he doubted.

"We have seen the Lord," they announced, but Thomas answered, "Except I shall see in his hands the print of the nails, and put my finger into the print of the nails, I will not believe."

Thomas was a doubter. But it had been Thomas who, when Jesus had proposed to go into Judea in the face of hostility that threatened his life, had said bravely: "Let us go also, that we may die with him."

Eight days after Jesus' first appearance to the group of disciples, they were again gathered in prayer. This time Thomas was with them.

Again, Jesus appeared in their midst and said, "Peace be unto you." Then turning to Thomas he said: "Thomas, reach hither thy finger, and see my hands, and be not faithless, but believe."

Thomas was convinced. "My Lord and my God."

"Because thou hast seen me, thou hast believed," Jesus said to him. "Blessed are they that have not seen, and yet have believed."

IT WAS GOOD to be home again in Galilee after so many months away. Peter and Andrew and James and John went at once to the lake. The waters were calm on this May morning.

"I go afishing," Peter said to the others.

"It is too early in the day for a catch," Andrew reminded him, but they could sail about until sundown.

"We need to be busy," James said quietly, and the others nodded. Jesus had said he would go before them into Galilee, but this period of waiting for their Lord to come back to them was a difficult one.

At sunset, they let down their nets. But this was not the night for fishing. They rowed about the lake, trying one spot after another, without success. Finally, toward morning, they headed for home. As they neared the shore, a stranger standing on the beach called to them, "Have ye aught to eat?"

"No," Peter called back, peering through the dim light.

"Cast your net on the right side of the boat, and ye shall find," came the answer from the shore.

Mystified, the weary men let down the net, and in a few moments began to draw it together and back into the boat. And the net was almost impossible to lift, so heavy was the catch of fish they had made.

John was the first to recognize Jesus. "Peter, it is the Lord!"

The Master! At once Peter dived into the water and swam rapidly toward his Lord.

"Bring of the fish, and break your fast," Jesus said to the four men, and once again they broke bread with the Master.

Once more Jesus shows himself to Peter and to others by the Sea of Galilee.

161

Jesus, his work accomplished, ascends into heaven.

This same Jesus shall so come again

THE DAY after Jesus had appeared to the eleven disciples as they prayed together, he came to them again and spoke with them concerning the meaning of the Scriptures. And he said to them, "Thus it is written, and thus it behooved Christ to suffer, and to rise from the dead the third day: and that repentance and remission of sins should be preached in his name among all nations, beginning at Jerusalem."

Then he led them out from Jerusalem, and they climbed the Mount of Olives until they could see Jerusalem laid out before them.

"Behold, I send the promise of my Father upon you: but tarry ye in the city of Jerusalem, until ye be endowed with power from on high."

Then he lifted up his hands and blessed them. And while he blessed them, he was parted from them and carried up into heaven.

And two men stood by them in white apparel. One of the men spoke: "Ye men of Galilee, why stand ye gazing up into heaven? This same Jesus, which is taken up from you into heaven, shall so come in like manner as ye have seen him go into heaven."

Going to the house of Peter and James, the disciples met in prayer with Mary, the mother of Jesus, and others of the women who had followed their Lord. And they went to the temple daily, with great joy praising and blessing God.

Within a century after the death of Jesus on the cross, Christianity had spread throughout much of the known world. Persecution, ridicule, death itself did not shake the faith or quell the joy of the early followers of Jesus, and his last promise sustained them, "Lo, I am with you alway, even unto the end of the world."

163

"Lo, I am with you alway, even unto the end of the world."